"I'll see you in New York"

TITANIC

The courage of a survivor

The
Edith Haisman
story

By her Son, David Haisman

First published in 1999 by Boolarong Press
With David Haisman

**National Library of Australia
Cataloguing-in-Publication data**

I'll see you in New York: Titanic: the courage of a survivor: the Edith Haisman story.

ISBN 0 646 33236 8.

1. Haisman, Edith. 2. Titanic (Steamship). 3. Shipwrecks - North Atlantic Ocean. 4. Survival after airplane accidents, shipwrecks, etc. 5. Shipwreck victims. I. Title. II. Title: Courage of a survivor. III. Title: Edith Haisman story. IV. Title: Titanic.

910.91634

BOOLARONG PRESS
35 Hamilton Road, Moorooka, Brisbane, Qld 4105

Layout and design by Mario Kyriacou
Cover illustration by David Haisman
Photos featured in the book are part of the Haisman Collection
Illustrations and images designed by David Haisman and Mario Kyriacou
Printed and bound by Watson Ferguson & Co., Brisbane

ABOUT THE AUTHOR

Edith Haisman, up until January 1997, was the world's oldest living survivor of the Titanic disaster, the author, David, being her youngest son. He has travelled the world for many years in the British Merchant Navy, in the capacity of Able Seaman and Quartermaster, finally serving as Mate and Relief Skipper on coastal tankers.

In 1959 he joined Cunard's White Star Line, as it was then known, and sailed on two of the world's largest liners, namely the Queen Elizabeth and Queen Mary. Whilst sailing on these great liners he served as 'lookout man', doing the same job as Fred Fleet, Titanic's 'lookout man'. These trips across the North Atlantic were over the same course as that taken by the Titanic and he has, on many occasions, witnessed the same weather conditions.

He later joined other ships of the line, on the Canadian run, stopping on some nights in the middle of vast ice fields, waiting for daybreak, before proceeding to the St Lawrence Seaway. It was during those times that the author would try to imagine what it must have been like for his mother, cramped up in a small lifeboat in freezing conditions.

Living in Southampton, he had spoken many times to Fred Fleet, who was a newspaper seller in the city, and well known by many seamen in the port. Fred Fleet had been an orphan and ended his sea career in 1936. Later, falling on hard times and losing his wife, he sadly committed suicide in 1965.

When compiling this life story of his mother, the author has used many years of his personal knowledge in sailing on these great ships, his knowledge of the port of Southampton, and his never-ending interest in the Titanic disaster.

His mother had told him throughout his life, along with other members of his family, vivid stories of that fateful night on 14 April 1912. She was 15 at the time and could well remember those terrifying cries for help as literally hundreds of men, women and children were dying together in those icy waters of the North Atlantic. These sounds were to haunt her for the rest of her life.

Throughout this story, nautical terms have been kept to a minimum, but where they are used, it is in modern day terminology.

He is grateful for all the input from his family, and the help from various friends, in piecing it all together.

This is how Edith told it and this is the way it was.

To Mum. From all of us.

*The Haisman family at the 60th Wedding Anniversary celebrations.
From left to right: Fredrick Jnr., Ken, Leo, Fredrick Snr., Geoffrey, Edith, Joy, John, Dorothy, Donald and David (Author).*

Contents

Chapter One
Iceberg **7**

Chapter Two
Capetown **25**

Chapter Three
London **35**

Chapter Four
Titanic - Day one **45**

Chapter Five
Titanic - Day two **53**

Chapter Six
Titanic - Day three **57**

Chapter Seven
Titanic - Day four **65**

Chapter Eight
Titanic - Day five 71

Chapter Nine
Titanic - Day six 75

Chapter Ten
New York 91

Chapter Eleven
Capetown 105

Chapter Twelve
Southampton 119

Chapter Thirteen
Simonstown 131

Chapter Fourteen
Australia 137

Postscript and
Acknowledgments 147

Chapter One

Iceberg

Her father stood in the doorway of their cabin and said to them both, 'There's talk that the ship has hit an iceberg'. It was those fateful words that were to change their lives forever. Edith and her mother, Elizabeth were sharing a two-berth second class cabin on board of the Titanic. Her father, Thomas, was sharing a cabin with another gentleman further along the passageway.

It was almost midnight on Sunday, 14 April 1912, when Thomas Brown, still in evening dress, made this announcement to his wife and daughter. Just 15 minutes previous to this, both women had been woken up by what could only be described as a shudder and several bumps. At that precise moment, Edith occupying the upper berth, switched on her bunk light, parted the surrounding curtains, and peered down at her mother lying on the bunk below.

Elizabeth had also heard the noises and, on turning on her own bunk light, stared up at her daughter in total bewilderment. Edith, quickly threw back her bed covers, swung her feet out and descended, step by step, down the little varnished bunk ladder to the cabin floor.

Edith crossed the cabin to the porthole and pulled the neat little curtains apart, opened the port glass, and stared out into the blackness. At first she could see nothing until her eyes became accustomed to the darkness and then gradually, she began to make out the ships lights reflecting far down on the water below. It was flat and calm with no wind and, looking up, she could see a mass of stars in the night sky. Looking down again towards the stern of the ship, she noticed a great deal of foam and turbulence as the ship's propellers churned up the water. The vessel was going full astern. This was causing tremendous vibration around the cabin with the clinking of glass, creaking and squeaking of wood panelling and other fittings about their room.

Edith drew her head back in from the porthole to enable her mother to see for herself that the ship was stopping. Elizabeth looked down at the water for a brief spell and then, drawing her head back in, crossed the cabin back towards her berth. Sitting on the edge of her bunk with a worried look on her face, she said to Edith in a somewhat shaky voice, 'I wonder what that is all about then?'.

At the forward part of the ship, the deck crew, firemen, trimmers and male emigrants had their accommodation situated there and would have experienced the impact with the iceberg more so than anyone else on board. It wouldn't have taken them long to realise that things weren't as they should be and many of them would have turned out of their bunks to investigate. Some of the crew had described the incident as like 'running aground' or like an 'anchor chain' rubbing against the ship's side. The more experienced seaman, familiar with this voyage across the North Atlantic, would know that couldn't be the case and would realise that they had collided with something extremely large. The 'heeling over' directly on impact had indicated that, and the chunks of ice on the forward well deck, had left none of them in any doubt that the ship had encountered a huge iceberg.

In the crow's nest, the two lookouts had watched the iceberg pass on the starboard bow and had felt the mast shudder on striking the iceberg. Their feelings at that time was that it had been a close shave and that perhaps the vessel had 'shelved off', giving no cause for any real concern. They remained in the crow's nest until being dismissed by the Officer of the Watch, some time later after the ship had stopped. On the bridge, Sixth Officer Moody had received the message from Fred Fleet in the crow's nest and immediately passed it on to First Officer Murdoch. He instantly ordered the wheel hard to port and put all engines at 'full astern'. A ship of that size, travelling at over 21 knots, would have responded to the wheel quite positively over a certain distance, but had only swung some 22 degrees before striking the iceberg.

Captain Smith was called to the bridge immediately, and going out to the starboard wing was just in time to see the iceberg disappearing far astern in the darkness. He ordered the carpenter to sound the forward tanks and asked other crew members to inspect all forward compartments.

Down in the engine room, the last few minutes had been hair raising, wondering what to expect next after being ordered to go full astern. They had still not heard from the bridge what the problem was although, the lurching and bumps felt below meant that they had struck something.

Up in the public rooms, some passengers were aware of a slight bump or two or a shudder as they put it, but it was nothing that caused any great concern. Some passengers at card schools and others at the bar enjoying a nightcap, stopped briefly before carrying on with what they were doing. Some other passengers, got up from their seats and went out to the promenade deck to meet others already out there, talking excitedly about an iceberg passing so closely as being almost able to touch it.

The ship's orchestra had almost finished playing for the night but their leader, sensing some unease amongst the passengers, decided to carry on for a spell with a ragtime selection. Stewards on duty up in the public rooms were approached now and then by the odd passenger inquiring as to why the ship had stopped. Their replies were much the same, saying that they would soon be on their way once they were clear of the surrounding icefield. There was also talk about how cold it had become and several were deciding to go to their cabins and turn in for the night. Some of the passengers were advised to do this as it was approaching midnight and most of the entertainment would be closing down for the night. There was after all, little to see out on the open decks anyway.

Down in their cabin, Elizabeth, sitting on the edge of her bunk, rose and crossed the cabin to turn on the main overhead cabin light. The excessive vibration experienced earlier had now stopped and the only sound audible was the faint whine of an electric motor somewhere far inside of the ship. The night air from the open porthole made the cabin feel colder and Elizabeth, sitting down again on the edge of her bunk, said to Edith, 'Pass me my dressing gown from the wardrobe, please dear'. After passing her mother's dressing gown to her, Edith crossed again to the porthole and looked out to see if anything else was happening. Once again, after her eyes became accustomed to the darkness, she could see that all was quiet, the turbulence had ceased and the ship was now motionless on a flat calm sea.

On closing the porthole, Edith crossed the cabin to sit alongside her mother on the lower berth, saying to her mother, 'Everything seems so quiet'. It was shortly after this that Thomas had tapped on their door and informed them about the iceberg. He had advised them to put on warm clothing and life jackets and to follow him back up on deck. Elizabeth looked at her husband in utter disbelief at his suggestion. Thomas, on the other hand, was not to be deterred and, on entering the room, reached up to the top of the wardrobe and pulled down the two life jackets there. Elizabeth was an extremely nervous person by nature and this action by Thomas wasn't helping matters any. Edith at 15 years of age was not too worried at this stage and obediently did as she was told, knowing her father never made any rash decisions.

Both women proceeded to put their warm topcoats on before Thomas began to help them on with their life jackets. Elizabeth remained speechless as her husband busied himself about her, adjusting the bulky life jacket and tying the tapes in front with a large bow. The life jackets were made up of cumbersome square chunks of hard cork, held together by stitched canvass and when placed over the head, hung from the shoulders and tied at the waist. With these on over their heavy clothing, both women looked and felt twice their size, causing Edith to giggle, forgetting the seriousness of the situation for a moment.

Before leaving their cabin to go up to the boat deck, Edith said to her father, 'Why aren't you wearing your life jacket father?', to which he replied, 'Don't let that worry you for the moment, my dear. Let's get you and your mother organised first and then I can get myself sorted out later'. This was typical of him, Edith thought. Always putting us first at all times. Making their way out of the cabin, they proceeded along the plush carpeted passageway to the first flight of stairs, which would take them to the upper second class promenade deck. From here there would be another four flights of stairs to the boat deck. At this time there were a few passengers moving about the passageways and stairs, some in evening dress, others with coats over night attire, and some with life jackets on. There was a bedroom steward with a tray of dirty cups and saucers balancing on the palm of one hand, tapping the doors with his knuckles of the other hand, calling out, 'Everyone up with life jackets on please!'. He continued with this until arriving at the night pantry at the far end of the passageway. There was little response, the whole scene quite relaxed with the odd quip about having a good night's sleep disturbed and others, not even answering the steward's call.

They continued up the stairs, with their carved banisters, and past beautiful oak panelling on the walls, passing other passengers returning to their cabins, remarking that it was too cold to remain on deck for any length of time. They arrived at the top of the final flight of stairs and stepped out onto the boat deck into the cold night air, joining a group of people already gathered around lifeboat no. 14. Thomas had noticed whilst in their cabin, the small notice behind the door, saying that occupants of that cabin would assemble at lifeboat no. 14 during any emergency.

Below their position on the boat deck, they could hear lively music coming from the Palm Court and Verandah Grill Restaurant area with Elizabeth remarking to her husband nervously, 'Some people don't seem to be too worried about this situation, Tom'. His reply was, 'It's better to be prepared in case things get out of hand and we may have to get into those boats'. Other people stood around indulging in light-hearted conversation as they watched some seamen take the covers off boats and prepare them for lowering into the water.

Edith was feeling tired after being woken from a deep sleep, and now between yawns, began to think about her comfortable bunk and said to Thomas, 'When do you think we'll be able to go back to bed father?'. 'Soon, dear, soon,' he replied. Her mother, however, was far from tired and was showing some considerable concern as the crew continued working on the boats. Her father, fully realising her mother's fears at the way things were developing, did his best to calm her down by saying that it wouldn't be too long before he would be tucking them both in for the night, once the emergency had been called off.

There was considerable talk about ice with one well dressed gentleman saying to another, 'I say, old man, I hear they're throwing ice around at each other down on the fore deck!'. With a grin his friend replied, 'Perhaps we'd better go down and join in the fun and warm ourselves up a bit'. The breaths of both men visible with puffs of vapour emerging as they spoke. There was also mention that some of the third class passengers at the forward end were leaving the well deck area, carrying suitcases and their belongings.

Up to this point in time, there had been no official indication that anything was wrong, other than some stewards directing passengers to go up on deck with their life jackets on. There had not been any alarm bells, hooters or announcements from ship's officers that there was a problem, hence the relaxed attitude of the passengers.

Edith and her parents continued to wait patiently, watching and listening to the goings on around them as more people arrived up on the boat deck. Many were still in evening dress and apparently in good spirits, attempting a witty remark now and then as the ship's orchestra continued to play lively music from the deck below. Amongst the chatter there was much wild speculation as to what had actually happened with one man saying, 'My steward tells me that we may have to abandon ship until repairs have been carried out, just as a safety precaution'. Hearing this, another man close by retorted, 'That's an extraordinary story if ever I heard one!'. And then went on, 'This ship is supposed to be unsinkable, in which case we're better off remaining on board, surely'. A third man listening to these remarks, joined in by saying, 'Perhaps we should let the crew get on with what they're doing and just take orders like everyone else'. However, passengers and crew alike were behaving in an orderly fashion although the look on Thomas's face revealed that he wasn't too happy the way things were developing.

On the bridge, Captain Smith had received word from the carpenter that air was rushing out of the vents from the tanks in the forward section, an indication that they were flooding. Accommodation and storerooms in the lower part of the bow section were also flooding and water was finding its way into the mailroom. It was indicated to the captain that everything was being done to lift the sacks of mail to a higher level by the mail sorters. Other reports coming to the bridge revealed that the forward most boiler room was also taking in water and, although watertight doors had been closed, the situation was looking worse by the minute. Captain Smith, turning to one of his junior officers, shouted, 'Get Mr Andrews up here right away!'. The junior officer didn't have far to go as Thomas Andrews, the Titanic's chief designer, nearly knocked him over on entering the chart room, clutching rolls of blue prints. He had been awake at the time of impact with the iceberg and knew, by the way the ship had shuddered, she just had to be damaged somewhere.

In the chart room beneath the glow of the soft orange light above the table, the blueprints were unrolled revealing the Titanic's innermost construction details. Captain Smith and Thomas Andrews leant forward together and began to scrutinise the ship's layout of the forward compartments and the adjacent areas. From the reports coming up to the bridge, it was becoming clear that the ship was taking in water along the first five forward compartments, which meant a fracture or fractures of almost 100 metres in length. Captain Smith, raising his head and looking at the ship's designer, said in a tight voice, 'What does it mean Mr Andrews?'. With an ashen look on his face, he looked at the captain and replied in utter despair, 'She could stay afloat with any four compartments flooded, but not with five'. He went on, 'The bulkhead between the fifth and sixth compartments only went as high as E deck and once it was flooded to that level, would overflow into the next compartment and so on throughout the whole length of the vessel. Both men looked at each other in the stark realisation that after just four and a half days into her maiden voyage, the Titanic was doomed. Captain Smith then asked Thomas Andrews in a choked voice, 'How long do you give her?'. Looking back towards the blueprints and scanning the plans before him, he replied, 'Two hours at the most'.

Just 45 minutes after the collision, the ship had taken on board well in excess of 10,000 tons of water. Captain Smith knew there wasn't a moment to lose and, going back into the wheelhouse, said to his officers, 'Gentlemen the situation is grave'. He then went on, 'She's going to founder. We must abandon ship! Clear away all boats and it's women and children first!'.

The ship's orchestra had now moved up to the boat deck as more and more people were finding their way there, and continued to play popular tunes from that era. Seamen continued to clear away the boats for lowering, as a slight incline towards the bow was now quite noticeable along the whole deck.

The night appeared to be very still now with the ship stopped, but very cold with several passengers returning to their cabins to put on extra clothing and some, unbelievably, returning to go back to bed. This was not to last, however, as ship's stewards, stewardesses and all other personnel were given strict orders that all cabins were to be vacated immediately, and all passengers told to proceed to the boat deck with life jackets on.

The crew were performing their duties in an orderly professional manner, treating all classes firmly but politely. Elizabeth was becoming increasingly distressed as more boats were being prepared for lowering and, once they were at deck level, people were ordered into them with a greater urgency. Thomas was doing his best to calm her down by saying, 'Don't upset yourself, my dear. I shall probably get into another boat once all the women and children are sorted out first'. He knew he didn't sound very convincing, but there was little else he could say at a time like this. Edith held tightly onto her father's arm with both arms, stamping first one foot and then the other, in order to maintain some circulation around her feet.

Lifeboat no. 14, their designated boat, had Fifth Officer Lowe in command. He was a Welshman in his late twenties and was well known as a bit of a disciplinarian, ordering people into the boat in no uncertain terms. His voice had authority and could be heard on more than one occasion, shouting at crewmen to 'Get a bloody move on!'.

In the first class public rooms, the emergency was still being treated as more of an inconvenience, rather than the disaster it was quickly becoming. Passengers were still finishing off their drinks and card games, whilst others were sitting around in life jackets, appearing to wait for the whole thing to be called off so they could get on with what they were doing. Many had assembled in the gymnasium and were being advised by the gym instructor to use the equipment to keep themselves warm.

Out on the boat deck more and more passengers were arriving from the lower decks as Elizabeth said to Thomas in a faltering voice, 'How on earth do they expect to get this lot into those tiny boats?'. Her husband could see her point but dared not say anything and answered, 'Its quite amazing just what those boats will hold'.

As people were being helped into the boats, there was suddenly an ear-shattering gush of steam blasting out of one of the waste pipes at the top of one of the funnels. There followed shrieks and cries with people ducking and reacting as though there had been an explosion somewhere. The release of steam from the engine room had been the result of a build-up of increasing pressure now that the ship had stopped, and it had to be vented off. This continuous deafening noise only made matters worse as all communications between officers, crew and passengers could only be heard by shouting through cupped hands. People were also now beginning to show signs of real fear at the prospect of the ship blowing up beneath them, not being able to understand why the steam was being blasted off.

After some 20 minutes or so, the roar of steam had eased to a strong but more acceptable hiss and once again the ships orchestra could be heard playing lively music through the din. The musicians were doing a superb job, showing great dedication to duty, as their efforts were having a calming effect on many passengers' nerves.

Up in the radio shack, both operators were having one of the busiest days so far during the voyage, going through a heavy work load, transmitting passengers' messages through this wonderful new medium of radio. The senior operator, Jack Phillips, had relieved Harold Bride earlier in the day and had continued with the never-ending demand for the transmitting of passengers' messages now that they were within range of Cape Race. Many of the messages sent were of a trivial nature and were merely sent to impress those friends and relatives in America, to show the wonders of ship to shore radio. Both operators had become irritable from long sessions, working the equipment with the incessant pips in their ears from the Morse code signals. During the day they had interruptions from other ships' operators breaking into their transmissions with ice reports and, due to their huge workload, some of these reports remained on their desk instead of on the bridge.

Harold Bride had arrived up in the radio shack just around midnight to relieve Phillips from his duties, when Captain Smith entered the radio room and said to both men, 'You had better send for assistance'. Phillips, wondering just how serious the situation was, replied, 'Do you want us to send out the distress call sir?'. 'Yes', replied the captain, 'Right away!'. Phillips immediately started sending out the Morse code signals CQD, recognised at that time as the international distress call. After a few minutes he turned to his commander and said, 'Shall I also try the new distress call of SOS sir?'. 'Yes', replied the captain, 'Use them both'.

The response to their distress call was almost immediate. Within minutes they had received several replies from ships within their range, the first from the German steamer, Frankfurt at approximately 12.20 a.m., but they gave no position. Others included a Russian tramp steamer, the CPR. liner, Mount Temple and the liner, Virginian. All of these ships had acknowledged the distress call but their distance from the Titanic was a major factor. The steamer closest to the Titanic was the Cunard Line's, Carpathia, steaming in the opposite direction out of New York, with 700 passengers on board bound for a Mediterranean cruise.

Harry Cotham, the Carpathia's radio operator, on picking up the Titanic's distress call, at first thought it was a mistake. He knew that he had better confirm the message before waking the captain otherwise, he would feel a bit stupid if he had got it wrong. He contacted the Titanic again to make sure that the ship was in difficulties and would need assistance. There was no doubt this time. The Titanic was sinking and they should proceed as fast as they could to the position given by Jack Phillips, as great loss of life may be imminent.

Captain Rostron was awakened by Cotham and there was a moment of disbelief, before he threw on his heavy coat over his pyjamas and rushed up to the bridge. He ordered the helmsman to alter course 180 degrees and then, on going into the chart room, worked out their distance from the stricken liner. The engine room was notified of the situation and they proceeded to give her 'all she had'.

These were dangerous waters at this time of the year and there was much ice about. Captain Rostron also had the safety of his own passengers and ship to think about, as he set his course for the Titanic's last reported position. The lookouts were doubled up and the Carpathia's usual cruising speed of 14 knots had been increased to 17 knots which was just about all she could take.

High up on the boat deck, Edith, pointing to the horizon, said excitedly, 'Look father, there's a light over there. Perhaps they will come over to help us!'. Thomas and Elizabeth both looked in the direction of their daughter's pointing finger and could also make out a light flickering on the horizon. Thomas, replying to his daughter, said, 'I do believe your right, my dear, let's hope so'. Several other passengers had also seen the light but it would always remain a mystery as to why that vessel never responded to the Titanic's distress rockets or Morse lamp signals.

The freighter Californian had stopped for the night in the same icefield as the Titanic, as her previous ice reports had indicated, leaving an apprentice ship's officer in charge on the bridge. He had seen what appeared to be a large liner on the horizon signalling with a morse lamp, but failed to reply as his own morse lamp was giving him trouble. It was during this time that a 'donkeyman' from the Californian's engine room, decided to go up on deck for a smoke and had seen rockets fired from the Titanic.

On the Titanic's boat deck there was now a greater urgency to get the women and children into the boats as increasing numbers were appearing up on deck from their cabins below. Down in the bow section where cargo holds and baggage rooms were situated there was extensive flooding with water creeping up the spiral staircase to the firemen's quarters. The lamp trimmer, who had been woken earlier by the impact with the iceberg, was now going along the passageways, banging the doors of sleeping watch-keepers, shouting, 'Everybody up! She's flooded out!'. Doors began to open with sleepy-eyed men peering out wondering what all the commotion was about. They were only clad in underpants or long Johns or, in some cases, stark naked, peering up and down the passageway from behind half open doors. They were soon to learn that things were looking bad, as water had reached the top of the spiral staircase and was now creeping along to their cabins, bringing along with it, bits of timber and wooden gratings. Without further ado, they grabbed what gear they could and, splashing through ankle deep ice cold water, made for the stairway leading to the upper decks.

Most of the deck crew were up and about attending to the lifeboats although some watch-keepers were still below in their bunks. The bosun was soon down there, banging on their doors and shouting out, 'Come on you bloody lot! Get a move on if you don't want a wet arse! She ain't got long!'. In boiler room no. 6 water had gushed in from the starboard side, taking with it chunks of coal from the coal bunkers, and splashing black oily slurry about the boiler room. The firemen and trimmers working the boilers were stripped to the waist and were splattered with this filthy ice cold black substance along with bits of coal and debris. The full shock of this torrent left many of them breathless and threshing about in the water after being knocked off their feet by the sheer force of it gushing into the boiler room. As the boiler room continued to flood, huge clouds of steam erupted as the water came into contact with the hot boiler casings, causing an acrid stench of coke-like fumes. The water, knee high and rising fast, meant only one thing to the engineer in charge. He had to get the men out of there as quickly as possible. 'Everyone out and up to the boat deck!', he shouted above the din of hissing steam and the cries from some of the men, as they began to scramble up the vertical iron ladders, coughing and spluttering as they went.

The engineers would remain below as long as possible, working pumps and generally trying to get on top of the situation. The way the water was rising was giving great cause for alarm, although it was hoped that the closed watertight doors would hold back most of the flow for the time being. Their main concern was to keep the essential services running like generators, to keep the pumps and lights working, although it was beginning to look as though the pumps would never keep up with the way the ship was flooding. All watertight doors had been closed by bridge control immediately after striking the iceberg, but they could be operated manually at any time. The chief engineer decided that they should be opened to inspect other sections of the engine room and, shouting above the noise, he said to two firemen, 'Open up the water-tight doors to boiler room no. 5 so that we can move about the bloody place!'.

Both firemen began to crank open the door which led to boiler rooms 1 and 2 and, once open, went on to boiler room no. 3 and so on until reaching boiler room no. 5. It was here that they heard tremendous rumblings and great popping noises from behind the bulkhead separating the two boiler rooms. The trimmers and firemen in this section were working frantically to draw fires and shut down dampers in their attempts to avoid any chance of an explosion. The fumes from the burning coals and hot ashes were a constant hazard as men were coughing and spluttering uncontrollably throughout the whole procedure. Despite this, they remained there with the heat and stench, hoping that their efforts may in some way, save the ship.

It was well after 1 a.m. when the chief engineer ordered one of his junior engineers topside to gain first-hand knowledge on how the situation was developing. He knew how busy the ship's deck officers would be at a time like this and, by getting a first-hand report back from one of his engineers, it would give him a better picture of how things were. At the stern of the ship, passengers were having a quieter time of it up to now, as compared to their counterparts at the forward end of the ship. The third class cabins at the stern would normally be the noisiest on board, caused by the vibration of the three huge propellers. After experiencing the ship going full astern just an hour ago, they would have thought, at that time, that the whole bottom was going to fall out of the Titanic, but now, all was relatively quiet with just the distant hiss of steam, from one of the funnels far up above the boat deck. There had been talk of chunks of ice being scattered all over the fore deck but this did not appear to concern anyone, many people not realising the significance of what that really meant.

More and more third class passengers were coming up from the working alleyway to join friends and relatives on the after well deck. The working alleyway ran practically the whole length of the ship on E deck and was used by the crew for services throughout the ship. This was the only route that the third class passengers could take to link up with those at either end, other than passing through second and first class accommodation. As they continued arriving on the after well deck, the extent to which the ship was flooding at the forward end, was giving rise for concern to some passengers, who set about finding their own way to the boat deck. Some of those arriving on the well deck from the forward end, were wet around their legs from wading knee deep in water in their efforts to pick up what gear they could from their cabins. A comment from one emigrant to another was, 'What's the matter Paddy? Getting too wet for you up the other end is it?'. 'Aye', came the reply, and then, 'It's bloody freezing as well'. And then lightheartedly, 'Perhaps you'd like to try it for yourself, although I don't recommend it'.

Those now attempting to find their way to the boats were having a hard time of it. Some were losing their sense of direction, and ending up back where they started from and others were ending up in the first and second class public rooms and being ordered back by stewards. There were also other groups that had arrived in the crews' quarters and others, finding themselves in the ship's main galley, promptly helped themselves to some of the delicacies there.

The class system in those days was such that many of the third class didn't expect to be considered until all other classes had been dealt with first and so, resigned themselves to just sit it out and wait until told to do otherwise. One of the third class stewards had led a group up through a maze of alleyways and several flights of stairs up to the boat deck, but on his return to repeat this assistance, was ordered to attend to the second class passengers first.

'Women and children first! The rest of you stand well back away from the boat!' was the cry from Fifth Officer Lowe as crew began to assist passengers into lifeboat no. 14. The increasing throng of people coming up to the boat deck was causing considerable concern to the officer in charge, as it was becoming apparent that there just wasn't going to be enough room in the boats to accommodate all of them. One woman, who was being helped into the lifeboat, changed her mind and decided to stay with her husband. Suddenly a huge hand grabbed her by the shoulder and a gruff voice said, 'There's only one way you're going missus, and that's in that bloody boat!' and then he added, 'Your old man stays where he is!'. Another woman was crying hysterically as she was forcibly led away from her husband by a seaman. He soothingly said, 'Don't upset yourself, love. You'll be seeing each other in New York before you know it!'.

Elizabeth had stopped crying, but still held onto Thomas with both arms clutching tightly around his waist, her face buried in his chest, not wanting to see what was going on. Edith still holding on to his arm, took fleeting glances along to lifeboat no. 12 which was just ahead of them, and watched the women and children awkwardly trying to get into the boat, helped by their menfolk. Edith was trying her best to remain calm, but her mother's present state wasn't helping too much, and she was dreading the moment when they would have to get into their boat and leave her father behind.

The first boat away was lifeboat no. 7, which was only half full. The First Officer had ordered this boat away, realising that time was running out and once in the water, could return to the ship and pick up more survivors. The next boat to follow was lifeboat no. 5 with Third Officer Pitman in overall charge of both boats and these were tethered together with a line, bow to stern.

Other boats were in the process of being lowered, swinging about clumsily with crew trying to steady them with oars pushed against the ship's side. There were several people shouting back at loved ones left on deck, others crying and sobbing loudly and the odd shout, now and then from the crew, telling people to sit down and keep still. There was a dog barking up on the funnel deck somewhere, a child crying loudly and the continuous hiss of steam from two of the ship's four funnels. The foremost funnel had now become silent and this could be due to the forward boiler rooms now being totally flooded. As the boats continued to descend in a jerky unsteady fashion, one woman decided to jump into a lowering boat. This would have been certain death as she almost fell over the side, but was miraculously grabbed by a crewman and a passenger and was left dangling over the black icy water, before being yanked back into the boat by the two men, amid shouts and screams.

On the great North Atlantic liners, a lookout was posted on the docking bridge, this being a small raised deck at the stern of the ship. It was here that the emergency steering gear was situated and the lookout was usually a quartermaster, who on this night had witnessed the huge iceberg pass by. After the Titanic had stopped, he remained where he was until he was ordered from the bridge to take a box of distress rockets up to the wheelhouse immediately.

Up in the first class staterooms and cabins, the rich and the famous were being helped on with their life jackets by their own personal manservants and maids. They were being advised on what to wear and what little comforts they may take along with them. They had first class stewards to take them to their lifeboats and stewardesses to help their wives and children. There were, however, some first class passengers that showed extraordinary courage, like Benjamin Guggenheim and Mr and Mrs Strauss who chose to stay behind and give up their place in a lifeboat for someone else.

Stewardesses were doing a wonderful job, escorting women and children to the boats from all classes and then returning below again, to repeat the operation until they were sure that everyone was out of their cabins. Thomas Andrews was seen just about everywhere, instructing passengers to put on life jackets and directing them to the boats. He stopped one stewardess and asked her why she wasn't wearing her life jacket. Her reply was, 'Well, I'm crew aren't I sir and it wouldn't look good in front of the passengers now would it, sir?'. Thomas Andrews replied, 'You're a woman and you will need to get into a lifeboat with the other women and children to lend assistance'. He went on, 'By wearing a life jacket you will be setting an example to others to wear theirs also'. Finally, with a great deal of urgency, he said to her, 'Now get one on! There's not a moment to lose!'.

There were also many bellboys standing in a group on the boat deck, smoking, chatting and laughing, between themselves, not really grasping the situation for what it was. Their average age would have been no more than 14 or 15 years of age and they had no idea what they were expected to do, other than to keep out of the way. They were neither men nor boys but they were crew and the chances of any of them getting into a lifeboat on this night was extremely remote. They would eventually, like all the other men left on board, have to take their chances, once all the boats had gone. As the passengers continued to be loaded into the boats, there was the hissing 'sound of a rocket, streaking into the night sky, lighting up everyone's faces as it burst into a shower of sparks high above them.

Captain Smith walked along the wing of the bridge and looked back towards the slowly continuing rise of the Titanic's stern. The scene before him revealed a completely crowded boat deck with passengers clambering into those boats remaining, still hanging from their davits in readiness for lowering. Turning away, with a feeling of utter despair, he walked back along the sloping deck and entered the wheelhouse. Glancing up at the clock, he noticed the time to be 1.20 a.m. and thought briefly, that just one hour and 40 minutes ago, the Titanic was steaming through the night, the pride of the British merchant fleet. Now she was mortally damaged and dying and from what he had just seen, she would take many with her when she took her final plunge. Letting his glance fall, he read the last details recorded on a small blackboard below the clock at the change of the watch. It read, 'Air temperature, 32 degrees. Sea temperature 31 degrees' and then below that, the engine revolutions and the ship's course.

The captain had altered course earlier in the day, taking the ship on a track some 16 nautical miles further south to avoid the reported icefield. His thoughts may well have been, if only I had maintained my present course, the chances are we would have reached New York. After leaving Southampton late and then the incident with the New York at dock head causing further delay, this made the voyage around one hour late. This may have been vital in avoiding the huge iceberg.

Fate had dealt him a lethal blow, brought about by a chain of events, totally beyond his control. Another thought that may well have crossed his mind was that on sighting the iceberg, if only the port engine had been stopped first and put full astern, she may have increased her swing to port avoiding serious damage. Other engine movements may well have helped her around the iceberg. This would be entirely dependent on how soon the ice was spotted in the first place, something he would never know. Besides it was all pointless now. The officer of the watch had reacted as any seaman may well have acted on the spur of the moment, that being putting her at full astern to lessen the impact.

He turned away from the small blackboard and went across to the forward part of the wheelhouse and watched her bow settling further down in the water. He felt sick to his stomach at what he was witnessing, knowing the whole blame would be his and that he would never live to tell his side of the story. The law of the sea states that the captain will always be the last to leave the ship after all others had taken to the boats. It was out of the question on this night, however, there being not enough boats in the first place, meaning many others would be remaining behind with him, and that was a certainty. Captain Smith turned away and walked back outside to survey the tragedy unfolding before him as the quartermaster and fourth officer set off another distress rocket with an ear-shattering hiss and a showering of sparks.

Walking through the cloud of white smoke left behind by the rocket, the captain went out onto the port wing of the bridge and, picking up the loud hailer, ordered boats pulling away, to return to the ship and pick up more passengers. Some acknowledged his call with a wave but took no action, others took little notice and remained where they were for fear of being sucked under by the sinking vessel.

Down in the engine room, the engineers were far too busy to think about anything other than keeping all the pumps operational, working valves and generally trying to maintain the essential services such as the ship's lighting. Without lights there would be additional chaos so unnecessary utilities such as fans and electric motors were switched off to conserve power. The chief engineer had now ordered everyone out of the engine room and to the lifeboats, leaving just the engineers to maintain the machinery. Within minutes of this order being given for all hands to vacate the engine room, there was a thunderous roar as the bulkhead between boiler rooms 5 and 6 suddenly gave way. Those trimmers and firemen still in that area were smashed against boiler casings and shipside stringers as the torrent rushed towards the bulkhead of boiler room 4. The watertight doors were still open at this point, resulting in water gushing through the restricted space at ever-greater force, bringing with it, bodies and all kinds of debris. There was nothing much anyone could do against such great odds, other than to attempt to close the remaining water-tight doors and to help their shipmates out of there. Amongst the steam and mayhem, men were wading about in waist high ice cold oily water with drums, rags, and bits of timber floating about. Shouts were heard above the din, 'Get up those ladders or you'll go down with her!'. Many of the men were in a state of shock, their movements sluggish after working in the intense heat of the boiler rooms, and now being subjected to ice cold water splashing about their bodies.

High up on the sloping boat deck, the ships orchestra continued to play lighthearted music as boats were lowered down to the water, and were seen to be pulling away from the stricken liner. Lifeboats 5 and 7 were well clear on the starboard side, as was boat no. 6 on the port side. Lifeboat no. 1, with only 12 persons in it, and lifeboat no. 8 with only 28 persons aboard were also well clear, not making any attempts to return to pick up additional passengers. Lifeboat no. 9 had almost its full capacity of 56 persons on board, which was the number of people the boats were designed to carry. Lifeboat no. 12 was lowered into the water with 40 women and children on board and later returned to pick up a further 30 people from the freezing water. The time had now arrived for Elizabeth and Edith to get into lifeboat no. 14 as the crew began to help the women and children into the boat.

Above:Dorothy and Edith.

Below:Thomas and Elizabeth.

The inscription of Elizabeth's photo reads, 'Elizabeth Catherine Brown Nee Ford b. S.Africa 1873 d. Rhodesia 1925 Titanic Survivor.'

Chapter Two
Capetown

Thomas William Solomon Brown was born in Blackheath, London in 1853. He was a widower and had two sons and two daughters from a previous marriage and, although Edith knew little of her father's background, she knew he had a brother who was a ship's captain and that he had drowned at sea. Thomas owned the Masonic Hotel in Worcester in the Cape Province and also later, the Mountain View Hotel in Capetown. He had shares in wine and brandy companies and many interests in cottage properties in False Bay and Muizenberg. He was a well respected businessman, well liked in the community and was also known to be a prominent Freemason. He was a short man of medium build with almost white hair and a bushy moustache to match, a round kindly face, a pleasant disposition and always smartly dressed.

Edith's mother was born, Elizabeth Catherine Ford and was 20 years younger than Thomas. She was related to a wealthy Afrikaans family by the name of Louw, who owned farms and dairies around Durban and the Durbanville areas. A story, passed on to Edith by her mother, was that her uncle who was a doctor, had boiled the flesh off of a dead native and had presented the skeleton to a well known London hospital, in the name of medicine. Elizabeth was of medium build and height and could be described as having a matronly and Victorian look about her, but nevertheless, she was an extremely loving and devoted person to those close to her. She had dark hair and blue eyes and could be described as being quite a nervous person. She loved her husband dearly and he returned that love with the utmost generosity, spoiling her and taking her on surprise trips and out with him to business functions. Since marrying Thomas, she had never wanted for anything and had made it a rule that she would never ever interfere with any of his business affairs. Theirs was a happy marriage and she knew how lucky she was to have such a kind and generous man such as Thomas.

Edith was born in the Masonic Hotel in Worcester on the 27 October 1896. She was a small child with slender limbs and, at times, could be described as being slightly underweight, although she remained completely healthy despite that. She was the first child in this marriage, followed by a sister, born four years later, also at the Masonic Hotel. Tragically, her sister died eight years later from diphtheria at the Mountain View Hotel in Capetown..

Edith was not unlike her mother in appearance but her hair was fair and she had her father's disposition. She was devoted to her parents and her whole upbringing was focused towards her one day becoming a young lady. She looked after her young sister Dorothy almost like a young mother and, at the time of her death, was totally devastated, as was her parents. It took them all a long time to come to terms with their loss.

The first decade of this century had seen many historical events around the world including the death of Queen Victoria after 63 years on the throne. Marconi had transmitted his first transatlantic wireless message and the Wright brothers had taken to the air. Rolls Royce and the Ford Motor Company were producing automobiles in ever-increasing numbers, bringing an entirely new mode of transportation to the streets around the world. The Boer War in South Africa had left much uncertainty and there was a bit of a slump with many businesses in the doldrums.

Elizabeth had always kept in contact with her sister and her husband who lived in Seattle. Her sister's husband was a manager in the National Bank of Seattle. Her letters to Elizabeth in the latter part of 1910 and throughout 1911 were full of praise at the way life in America was booming. She had suggested many times that they should move out there and start up their own hotel business. As a result, Thomas and Elizabeth had many discussions over several months, weighing up the prospects of starting up a new business venture in a foreign country. Elizabeth was becoming more convinced, as time went by, and thought it to be a good move for them. Thomas, on the other hand, was a bit more reluctant to start with, possibly due to his age. He was approaching 60. He knew that Elizabeth was not one to try and force the issue and would never try to interfere in any way in his business interests. He was, however, very much aware of how excited his wife was at the prospect of a new life in Seattle.

Realising the quiet life Edith and his wife were living, he decided that it may just be the right thing to do and besides, things were a bit slow in Capetown at that time.

One beautiful morning in Capetown, Thomas, dressed in topper and tails, and swinging his silver-topped walking cane, strode down Adderley Street towards the Union Castle Shipping Line offices. He had worked out that if he could arrange a passage to England within the next few months, he stood a good chance of booking a passage on that great new liner that everyone was talking about.

Thomas had read in the Capetown Argus that the Titanic would be sailing from Southampton on 10 April. Working it out, he realised that they would have to sail on the Saxon at the end of February to enable them to spend a few weeks in London, to shop around those wonderful stores in Oxford Street and Bond Street and do a bit of sight seeing. Standing outside the shipping offices, Thomas looked along Adderley Street and up at Table Mountain, which looked as always, quite spectacular in the early morning sunshine.

The top of the mountain was draped in cloud cover, known as the 'table cloth' and, at one end, Lions Head could be seen poking through a ring of cloud near its top. Turning away from this wonderful view, he entered the shipping office and then suddenly felt very faint. He was forced to sit on a chair just inside the entrance. A young clerk came over to him and said in a clipped South African accent, 'Are you all right, sir?' and then went on, 'You do look a bit pale, sir. Would you like a glass of water?'. Thomas looked up and wiped his brow with his handkerchief. He replied in a shaky voice, 'I'm fine. A glass of water would be good. Thank you'. He still felt a bit shaky when the young clerk returned with the water but after he had taken a few sips, his colour slowly returned and he began to feel better. He had never had a feeling like this before, it was best described as a combination of panic and fear, but why? Feeling almost fully recovered, he got to his feet and went about the business of booking their passage to England.

On completing his bookings, he went out into the bright sunshine and began to walk back up Adderley Street, much slower this time, still not understanding what must have come over him a short while ago. He stopped a bit further along the street and again looked up at the mountain with its slate grey rock faces, its light purples and dark greens as a backdrop, feeling that he would miss this place once away from it. He started walking again, faster this time, realising that if things didn't work out they could always come back and he would make provision for such an event by leaving some of his stock here to mature. He entered the hotel at the front entrance and immediately saw his wife and daughter arranging flowers in the lobby. Going up to them, he embraced them both and, unable to hold back his excitement, said to them, 'It's done! We sail for England at the end of February!'.

That afternoon after all of the excitement Edith was sitting upstairs looking out of one of the windows of their private apartments, down at the street below. There was a penny whistle band passing below, beating drums and dancing as they went. They were always fun to watch with their lively carnival atmosphere, and Edith was quite enjoying the spectacle passing below her from her vantage point. Her mother entered the room and stood behind her to also take in the entertainment down on the street. As she leant over Edith she said to her, 'Do you think you will miss Capetown, my dear?'. To which her daughter replied, 'I don't really know, mother. I do like it here, but I'm also looking forward to our trip to America as well'. She went on, 'Especially on that wonderful new ship that everyone is talking about'. Then turning away from the scene below them, she looked at her mother and inquired, 'Do you think father really wants to go'. Elizabeth replied, 'I'm sure he does, my dear'. 'Your father would never do anything that he hasn't thought about first. That's one of the reasons why he's been so successful in everything he does.' Finally she said, 'If it's as good as they say it is in America, then we've nothing to lose and everything to gain'. With that, both women continued to look out of the window at the carnival below them.

Thomas had been busy these past few weeks, arranging all his finances, especially those holdings in the various wine and brandy companies. He was a shrewd businessman, taking care to leave those shares behind that would take longer to realise profits, but were considered to be safe. They may well come in handy if things don't work out in Seattle, he thought. He had little trouble in finding a buyer for his hotel, which was considered a good buy in the hotel business. He sold for a final sum of 14 000 pounds which was considered a good price at that time. He also had little difficulty in selling his toyshop, situated just off of Adderley Street, which was destined to become a barber shop.

One evening before departure, Thomas was having a drink in the bar of his hotel with an old business acquaintance of his. His friend said to him, 'I've known you for many years, Tom, and I've never known you to make a decision without thinking about it first'. He went on, 'To sell up everything at your age and to embark on a new business venture in another country must have left you with many sleepless nights'. After taking a sip of his brandy he went on, 'It's a courageous thing to do, Tom, I'll grant you that, but aren't you comfortable enough here, without going through all those uncertainties of setting yourself up again?'.

Thomas swirled his own brandy around in the bottom of his glass thoughtfully, puffing gently on his cigar, before finally answering his friend by saying, 'George, I could have stayed here in the Cape for the rest of my days and remained reasonably contented, but things are slow here at the moment and I want to give my wife and daughter a better chance in life before I get much older'. He then added with a chuckle, 'Besides, there's plenty of steam left in the old fellow yet and, no doubt, you'll be reading about me in the Capetown Argus when I've made my fortune'. With that, both men had a good laugh with Thomas gently patting his friend on the back saying, 'Come on, my friend. Let's drink to better days!'.

It was on a Thursday around lunchtime, on 26 February, when they arrived at the Union Castle Berth in Capetown Docks. It was a bright sunny day and a stiff south-westerly breeze was blowing across the harbour as they were helped on board the Saxon by two Negro porters. The Saxon was no stranger to them as they had travelled on her before on past trips to England. Once on board they were shown to their usual first class cabins by the senior steward. They had little luggage for this voyage other than that which was considered necessary until they reached London. Once in London, they had plans to completely outfit themselves with new clothes, and to purchase everything else that they would be needing for their new lives in America. Thomas would also purchase linens, crockery and silverware to be shipped out with them on the Titanic for his planned hotel enterprise in Seattle. Once they were settled in their cabins, they decided to go up on deck for a stroll and to have their final look at Capetown before sailing time.

At around 3.30 p.m. two tugs had arrived and positioned themselves alongside of the ship in readiness for departure. At exactly 4 p.m. the Saxon began to move gently away from the berth, edging her way around the rocky breakwater and finally, releasing the tugs, headed for the open sea. The Browns stood together on the after end of the promenade deck and for some considerable time looked back at Capetown. Table Mountain had no cloud cover on this day and was etched against a beautiful cloud-speckled blue sky, as if to give them all a final lasting impression of the Capetown they were now leaving, slowly fading away in the distance.

Edith, turning to her father said, 'Do you ever think we'll come back, father?'. Thomas, turning to look at his daughter replied, 'If things go as well as I'm hoping they will my dear, then I don't see any reason why we can't come back here once in a while for a holiday and to see old friends'. Elizabeth joining in to the conversation then added, 'Perhaps things will improve here over the next few years and your father may wish to come back for his retirement'. And then looking at her husband, smiling and said, 'If he knows what that is!'. Thomas gave one of his little chuckles and looking back towards Capetown said, 'That may be so, my dear. That may be so'.

That evening, and throughout the following two days, they were to experience the 'Cape rollers' conditions well known by sea travellers in those regions, comprising of huge troughs and heavy swells, leaving many passengers seasick. Edith and her father managed to get to the dining saloon for meals most of the time, not feeling too badly, but Elizabeth couldn't face food and remained below for most of the time. On the third day out from Capetown, sea conditions had eased and more and more passengers were coming up on deck to enjoy the fine weather. Elizabeth finally arrived up on deck and joined her husband and daughter who were sitting in deck chairs on the promenade deck. Thomas turned to face her as she approached saying, 'Are you feeling any better this morning, my dear?'. Elizabeth, still a little pale, replied, 'Oh yes, much' and then added with her sometimes dry sense of humour, 'If you're going to get seasick, then you're going to get seasick!'. She then went on, 'The only difference between third class and first class is that you pay more for the privilege!'. They had a laugh over that, Thomas noticing that his wife was almost back to her old self, and suggesting that perhaps she try a little breakfast.

After breakfast, leaving his wife and daughter in deep conversation with some other ladies in one of the public rooms, Thomas made his way to the Purser's office. He knew the Purser from previous voyages and on arriving at his office leant on the counter and said cheerfully, 'Good morning, Purser. How are you this fine day?'. The Purser looked up from a sheaf of papers spread out in front of him and replied, 'A very good morning to you, sir. I trust everything is well?'. 'Absolutely!', replied Thomas, and then went on, 'I thought I would inquire as to what you may know about the Titanic. They say she's unsinkable according to the press. What do you think of that?'. The Purser, a slightly balding man in his early fifties, looked over the top of his glasses, replying, 'If you ask me Mr Brown, I would say that the ships they're building these days are getting far too big and one day, I shouldn't wonder, there will be a serious mishap'. He then went on, 'Apparently the Titanic has been built along the same lines as her sister ship the Olympic, although its been reported that she is slightly bigger and more luxurious'. He continued, 'Mind you Mr Brown, she will be a wonderful ship for passengers but, for myself, I wouldn't like to serve on her'. He added, 'There's talk that she will be making round trips from Southampton to New York in 16 days and with a crew of over 800. You would never get to know anyone'. He added finally, 'No, Mr Brown, she's not for the likes of me. Give me the old Saxon any day. It's just like one big happy family on board here, and that's a fact!'. With that the Purser continued to shuffle some papers around and, on turning, said to Thomas, 'Excuse me, Mr Brown while I just pop these into the safe'. 'Certainly,' said Thomas, 'Go right ahead'.

The Purser crossed to the safe in the opposite corner and opened the door, placing the sheaf of papers in his hand into a box inside. With his back to Thomas, he continued the conversation by saying, 'I hear from the chief steward, in just passing you understand, Mr Brown, that you yourself are hoping to sail on the Titanic next month if I'm not mistaken?'. Thomas knew from past experience on board ships that they were always good for gossip and the Saxon was no different. He didn't mind, however, and felt a little proud at the prospect of sailing on such a great liner as the Titanic. Replying to the Purser's inquiry he said, 'Well that's the plan if the Americans don't buy up all the tickets first'. The Purser said, 'That's the trouble Mr Brown, the Americans seem to be the only people with any money these days, and buy up everything in sight'.

Just before the Purser closed the door of the safe, Thomas caught sight of his Gladstone bag just inside of the door with all their worldly possessions inside. It contained thousands of dollars in hard cash, jewellery and many gold sovereigns along with several important documents. In addition to this, he had about his waist, a money belt with cash and gold sovereigns sewn into his several waistcoats and morning coats. Elizabeth also had gold sovereigns sewn into many of her outdoor garments, this being quite normal practice for wealthy people travelling in those days. The Purser continued his conversation by saying, 'The Managing Director of White Star Line, a Mr Bruce Ismay, has indicated to the press that a third liner is to be built for the North Atlantic trade and she may be even bigger'.

The Purser was now warming to the topic saying, 'You mark my words, Mr Brown, they're building these ships far quicker than they used to in their attempts to capture the North Atlantic trade, now that the Germans have entered the race'. Thomas, nodding slowly, said 'Yes, yes. You may indeed be right, however, I must take my leave of you and join the ladies up on deck'. Moving away from the counter, his parting words were, 'It's been interesting talking to you, Purser, and a real pleasure. Good day to you'.

Before stepping out on deck, Thomas stopped by the entrance of the lobby and observed the ship's progress chart enclosed in a glass case. He noticed that the Saxon had travelled 410 nautical miles in the past 24 hours giving her an average speed of 17 knots. Not bad for an old girl, thought Thomas as he went out on deck to join the ladies. As the Saxon continued north towards the equator, the weather improved with the swimming pool becoming popular with passengers, as were the many deck games and competitions being organised. Edith and her mother took part in some of them, Thomas preferring to just watch, getting as much fun as a spectator. The weather remained fine as they crossed the equator, with those wonderful balmy tropical nights, making this a happy time for all three of them. Their memories of South Africa were becoming less frequent.

A week after crossing the equator, they were able to see the coast of West Africa and later passed the township of Dakar. Several days later the ship dropped anchor off Las Palmas in the Canary Islands to pick up provisions and mail. Thomas bought some trinkets for Elizabeth and castanets and a jewel box for Edith from a 'bum boat' that came alongside. After just a few hours, the Saxon weighed anchor and proceeded on her voyage north. The weather over the next few days became decidedly colder as the winter months in the Northern Hemisphere were not quite over yet. On entering the Bay of Biscay, it lived up to its name for heavy seas, causing many passengers to go down again with seasickness. Elizabeth appeared to fare better this time and managed to get to the dining saloon after the first day. When the Saxon entered the English Channel, the heavy weather had eased off although there was a cold easterly wind.

The voyage was coming to an end and, after dinner on their last night, they decided to go up to the promenade deck to look at the lights along the shoreline.

They saw a ship's officer coming along the deck and Thomas decided to ask about berthing in the morning. 'Good evening', said Thomas, 'Would you be kind enough to let me know the time of berthing in the morning?'. 'Certainly, sir', came the reply, 'We're due alongside in the morning at 6 a.m. 'Thank you', replied Thomas. He then asked what the cluster of lights was off the port side. The officer, looking in the direction of Thomas's outstretched arm replied that it was Weymouth. Further along towards the port bow it was possible to see the flashing light of the Needle's Lighthouse on the Isle of Wight. The officer explained that the ship would be slowing down shortly to pick up the pilot at 4 a.m. With that, Thomas thanked the officer for the information and bid him goodnight as they went down below to the warmth of their cabins.

The Saxon berthed right on schedule on the morning of 17 March and when passengers awoke, they could look out of their portholes at the green dock sheds of berth 46 outside. It was a very cold morning with a fresh north-easterly blowing and, with daylight approaching, one could see a completely blue cloudless sky. Disembarkation was at 8 a m. and after an early breakfast the passengers said their farewells to the dining and bedroom stewards. Thomas tipped those serving his family generously as always. After organising their luggage to be taken ashore, Thomas went up to the Purser's office to collect his Gladstone bag and to say his farewells to the Purser and his assistant. On shaking hands, both men wished him and his family bon voyage on their coming trip on the Titanic.

After leaving the ship, they travelled to Southampton Railway Station and caught the 11.30 a.m. train to Waterloo, passing through Winchester and the beautiful Hampshire countryside. They arrived in London at 1 p.m. They caught a hackney cab, this being their first experience of travelling in an automobile. On their previous visits they had always driven in horse-drawn carriages. They chugged over the Thames by way of Waterloo Bridge, past Lancaster Place, on to The Strand, in to Aldwych and then along Southampton Row, finally stopping in Russel Square, outside of the Russel Hotel. On arrival, a porter came out to meet them.

Painting by David Haisman of the Titanic leaving Southhampton.

Chapter Three

London

Once settled into their hotel, Thomas spent the next few days booking their voyage on the Titanic and organising the shipment of hotel items to be loaded on at Southampton. His intention was to travel first class but that was fully booked. He could not believe his luck to find that their three second class tickets were the last to be sold, according to the booking clerk. Now that he had done all that was required for the passage, the family set about getting themselves completely kitted out in new clothes.

They shopped in Knightsbridge, Mayfair and Chelsea, Elizabeth and Edith purchasing wool serge, high-necked and full length fitted coats, and double-breasted full-length coats with velvet cuffs and lapels. They bought hats to match, some with feathers, others with wide brims and some with lace face nets. They both had a passion for leather calf length, button-up boots, which were very fashionable at that time.

Thomas did the bulk of his shopping in Jermyn Street, St James's, and bought several custom made tailored suits on Saville Row. With his top hat and tails and silver-topped walking cane, he looked every bit the gentleman he was. The three of them had thoroughly enjoyed themselves these past few days looking around the shops and setting themselves up for their new life in America. Thomas had worked it all out very well knowing that London was one of the best places in the world for quality goods in those days.

Their stay at the Russel Hotel was always a pleasant experience and, unlike other hotels of similar standing, there was no air of snobbishness about the place. The staff were very friendly and Thomas knew some of them from his previous visits to London. There were several Cockneys working there and, with their fast wit, there was never a dull moment. Nothing was too much trouble for them.

The hotel had an excellent reading room with a Victorian grandfather clock, oak-panelled walls, oil portraits and thick pile carpet. There were glass cabinets around the room with a good selection of books, this being Elizabeth and Edith's favourite place when not sightseeing. Up on the first floor, the Browns occupied two rooms, thickly carpeted with drapes, inlaid mahogany furniture, fine bedspreads and an excellent view across Russel Square.

The weather had turned out fine and was mild for the time of the year, inviting them out for pleasant walks along Southampton Row and Bloomsbury Park. The buds were breaking out on the plants and trees and there was a feeling of spring in the air. Edith enjoyed these walks which gave her an opportunity to wear her new clothes and to look at other fashionable ladies walking with their gentlemen in the park.

One afternoon, after a visit to the British Museum, they returned to the hotel and sat in the lobby reading the various newspapers all reporting the latest on the Titanic. There were many exaggerated stories on her interiors and spaciousness, but the general opinion was that is was an unsinkable luxury liner, where passengers would be pampered all the way to New York. One article that Thomas was reading stated that the White Star Line director, Bruce Ismay, would be travelling on her for her maiden voyage, along with the ship's chief designer, Thomas Andrews. There were also lists of the names of the rich and famous that would be travelling on her and it all made impressive reading.

One time, as they were shuffling through the pages of the different newspapers in front of them, one of the waiters brought them a tray of tea and biscuits. On setting the tray down and noticing the pages spread out before them, he remarked to Thomas, 'She's a wonderful ship, ain't she, sir?'. Thomas replied, 'She certainly is by all accounts'. The waiter went on as he set out the tea pot and cups and saucers in front of them, 'Beggin' your pardon sir, but I understand that you and your good ladies will be sailing on this wonder of the high seas, if I'm not mistaken?'. Thomas, looking up from his newspaper, replied, 'Yes, that's correct'. He was thinking how news travels as he had just made a brief mention to the assistant manager when they arrived. Elizabeth looked at her husband, breaking out with a smile as Edith continued to flick through the pages of a paper.

During their last few days in London, they visited the Royal Opera House, Hampton Court Palace, the Botanical Gardens at Kew and the Tower of London. There was so much to see but time was running short. However, they had managed to visit those places they were eager to visit on this trip. It was now 9 April and tomorrow they would be travelling down to Southampton to join the Titanic. It was decided that they would spend the rest of the time at the hotel and enjoy the comforts it had to offer and have an early night before their big day tomorrow.

Edith could not remember ever seeing her mother and father so happy as they were that night at dinner. They chatted and laughed and generally discussed what the future may hold for them in America. Edith, now 15 years of age, was taking more of an interest in things and wanted to know what the social life would be like on board the Titanic. She asked her father, 'Do you think there will be much entertainment on the ship, father?'. Thomas, tilting his soup plate to finish off what was left replied, 'I should think so my dear, possibly every night'. He went on, 'They have an orchestra on board and I doubt very much that they will just perform for the first class only'. Elizabeth, dabbing the corners of her mouth with her napkin, added, 'It's a pity we couldn't get first class tickets for the voyage, Tom'. Thomas replied, 'Yes, that was unfortunate, although the booking clerk did tell me that the second class on the Titanic was as good as the first class on most transatlantic liners'.

Elizabeth replied, 'It certainly looks that way if those newspaper reports are anything to go by'. After their meal, they went into the lounge for coffee and another look through the newspapers. Thomas went into the bar and made conversation with some gentlemen there, always enjoying a brandy and cigar after his meal. Back in the lounge, Edith and her mother continued to read the various reports about the Titanic and her departure the next day. There were glowing reports about her luxurious public rooms, sauna, gymnasium and swimming pool. The reports invariably described her as unsinkable. Edith, reading some of the articles, wondered if there would be any other young people her age travelling on the ship which was fully booked and no doubt would include a few young people. Up to this point, her life had always been closely connected to her parents, whom she adored, but the time was approaching when she wanted to meet more people of her own age.

A short while later, Thomas returned to the ladies in the lounge and, noticing Elizabeth still reading the paper, said to her, 'You don't know how lucky you are to be going on this wonderful ship'. His wife looked up over her paper, a little puzzled, before he went on, 'However, I've changed my mind and tomorrow I'm going to cancel the trip and go back to Capetown!'. Edith looked at her father in dismay, her mother, knowing the look on Thomas's face, burst out laughing, exclaiming, 'Just you try it, Tom Brown!'. And then still laughing, went on, 'Edith and I will tie you up in your bed tonight when you're asleep!'. Thomas beginning to chuckle, replied 'Now would I do such a thing?'. They had an early morning call at 6 a.m. and, after dressing, went down to the dining saloon for their early pre-arranged breakfast. They ate well, having a good English breakfast, and then returned to their rooms to pick up their hand luggage and make sure they hadn't left anything behind.

On arriving down at the reception area, Thomas was handed his Gladstone bag from the assistant manager as two porters organised their luggage for them, taking it out to the waiting cab. 'Thank you for a pleasant stay,' said Thomas as he took his bag, and then added, 'Perhaps we'll meet again some time'. With that, he shook hands. The assistant manager replied, 'It's been a pleasure, sir!' And then went on, 'We are always delighted to have our regular guests stay with us'. And then finally saying, 'On behalf of the staff and myself, we would like to wish you and your good ladies, Bon Voyage and a happy life in America'. Thomas thanked him and went out through the front entrance to join his wife and daughter, who were already getting into the cab, as a porter held the door open for them. The Cockney porter holding the door open for Thomas said, 'When will we be having the pleasure of your company again Mr Brown?'. 'That will depend on how things go my friend', replied Thomas, and then added with a bit of fun, 'But when I do, I expect to see you as manager!'.

With that, the porter gave out a cheeky laugh and spluttered, 'Cor, that'll be the day!' and then added, 'You never know your luck, ain't that right Mr Brown?'. Thomas now laughing along with him, finally said, 'With your gift of the gab, my friend, you'll make it anywhere' and then after shaking him by the hand, pressed a shilling into his palm. Taking his place in the cab alongside Elizabeth, the porter in a half saluting gesture, called out, 'Thank you very much, sir and you and them good ladies have good trip and tell me all about it when you come back!'. With those parting words, the cab spluttered into life, amid clouds of blue smoke and began its journey down Southampton Row.

It was another beautiful spring morning as they motored past Bloomsbury Park on their way to Waterloo Station. Thomas pulled out his gold pocket watch on its long chain and noted the time at 7.45 a.m. They were in good time, the boat train not due to leave Waterloo until 8.30 a m. which should then arrive alongside of the Titanic in Southampton at 10.15 a.m. On arrival at Waterloo Station, a railway porter met them as they got out of the cab and, on a nod from Thomas, he began to load their baggage onto his cart. 'Which platform are we looking for sir?' asked the porter as he hoisted another bag up. 'The one the boat train will be leaving from,' replied Thomas. 'Right you are, sir. That'll be platform 10,' said the porter, wheeling his cart away, as Thomas paid the cab driver.

There were many groups of people standing along the whole length of the platform as the porter led them to the first class compartments. There was the occasional whiff of coal smoke and steam from the engine, just a few carriages further along, as a gentle breeze swirled about the station. They arrived at their designated compartment, their baggage loaded into the carriage and smaller items put into the luggage nets above the seats. After tipping the porter for his services, they sorted themselves out and settled down for the journey. Soon after, there was a final slamming of carriage doors, followed by a prolonged whistle from the guard, a slightly jerky forward movement and they were on their way.

As they gathered speed, they began to clear greater London and the buildings and bridges became fewer as they headed into the countryside. Thomas, peering out of the carriage window, pondered on what may be in store for them once they had arrived in Seattle. Seattle was becoming an important financial centre of the Pacific north-west or so he had been advised by his business associates back in South Africa. With the Alaskan gold rush and the opening of the Panama Canal, the hotel business should do extremely well, all things being equal. Settling further back into his seat, he concluded in his mind that this was definitely the right move for the three of them and they had a great future to which to look forward.

Elizabeth, sitting alongside her husband, had her head back on the headrest of the seat, and her eyes closed. She wasn't asleep, however, just thinking about the coming trip on the Titanic and the many interesting people who would also be travelling. As she listened to the clatter of the carriage wheels beneath her, she thought of the shipboard gossip that would no doubt accompany them on this voyage.

Smiling to herself, she knew that most of what one heard could be taken with a grain of salt. She slowly drifted into a light sleep.

Edith, sitting opposite her mother and father, was also looking out of the carriage window as they left the Berkshire countryside and entered the county of Hampshire. Passing the market town of Basingstoke, her thoughts were also on the Titanic and what kind of future was in store for her. She would be 16 in October and perhaps, she would be helping her mother in the hotel, much the same as she did in Capetown. She thought of the Titanic and wondered if there would be dancing in the evening, giving her an opportunity to wear one of those pretty dresses she had bought in London. She also wondered whether any other young people her own age would be travelling. Maybe they could become friends.

It was going to be a completely new way of life for her and she was finding it difficult to contain her excitement at times. As the train continued its journey through the lush green Hampshire countryside, they passed England's ancient capital of Winchester. Some 15 minutes later, they passed through the outskirts of Southampton, entering the Northam Goods Yards. It was this district from which many of the crew of the Titanic would come. Southampton had a long tradition of providing crew for the big liners in the port. On this morning, true to seafaring tradition, there would be many hangovers after a last night ashore 'booze up' in many of the local pubs. The train began to slow down as it approached Southampton Terminus Station. The train continued to slow down as it passed the South Western Hotel on its right, crossed Canute Road, and entered the Southampton docks. It was here, almost at this point, that King Canute had tried to stop the tide from advancing and the actual place is marked by a public house, called appropriately, The King Canute.

Edith standing at the carriage window was full of excitement as the train slowly wound its way through dockland. She could now see several ships in the docks and passing close to a Union Castle liner, pointed and shouted excitedly, 'There it is!'. Thomas joining her at the window and looking in the same direction, said gently to his daughter, 'I don't think so my dear'. Then he added, 'She would have to be bigger than that and have two more funnels'. Edith began to laugh, saying to her father, 'Of course! I forgot that'. Elizabeth, laughing along with her daughter, added, 'Put it down to excitement my dear'.

The train, still moving slowly, changed direction giving them a different view with Edith pointing once again and saying excitedly, 'That must be it, father!'. Thomas again leaning over his daughter to look out of the window said, 'Yes! That's her'. Elizabeth, also moving forward to take a look, exclaimed, 'My God! She's enormous'. They had an excellent view, along with the other passengers on the train, who were all staring out of the windows at this huge ocean-going liner that many of them would soon be boarding. The Titanic looked serene, as she lay moored alongside Berth 43, with her huge black hull rising out of the water. Her white superstructure, towering over everything on the dockside, dwarfing cranes working her cargoes. Her four great buff-coloured funnels stood proudly above everything else, with smoke curling lazily from their black shiny tops. It was indeed a breathtaking sight for those on the train, seeing this mighty liner for the first time.

Their train, now moving forward at walking pace, entered the great cargo and passenger shed alongside the Titanic and, once inside, finally came to a halt. Inside the terminal, it was a hive of activity with a mixture of dock workers and passengers moving about, baggage being wheeled to and fro and the general atmosphere created by a mass of people on the move. As Thomas stepped from the carriage to help the ladies on to the platform, a porter arrived on the scene with his trolley, to help them with their luggage. 'First class gangway, is it sir?' asked the porter. 'No,' replied Thomas, 'We're for second class'. 'Then second class it is, if you'll follow me, sir?' Leaving behind the sounds of the engine, puffing and wheezing, they followed the porter to the great doors on the other side of the shed. Thomas, carrying his Gladstone bag, stopped briefly and took out his pocket watch and noted that it was 10.20 a.m. They had made good time he thought and, as the ship didn't sail until 12 noon, they would have plenty of time to settle in and look around the ship.

They continued to follow the porter to the foot of the gangway where a portable desk was situated behind which two officials sat. On arrival there, Thomas produced his tickets and also the paperwork regarding the hotel items that were to be loaded into the ship's hold. He inquired about his crates, which were being sent down from London, and the White Star official, after leafing through some cargo manifests, confirmed that they had already been loaded. On returning his paperwork, the official said, 'May you and your good ladies have a pleasant voyage, sir'. After thanking him, the three of them moved towards the bottom of the gangway to pause for a moment, to look at the huge black hull running along the full length of the dockside.

Looking up at the white superstructure high above them, they could see rows of portholes with the morning sunshine glinting on their brass rims. Higher up, they could see many passengers leaning on the ship's rail, shouting, now and then, to friends and loved ones down on the dockside. Edith, looking up in utter amazement, said to Thomas, 'How on earth does it float father?'. Thomas, with one of his little chuckles, answered his daughter by saying, 'Let's hope that it does my dear or we'll never see New York!'. Elizabeth moved forward first and stepped on to the foot of the gangway and started to walk up the slight slope towards the ship's open shell doors. Thomas beckoned to Edith to follow her mother up the gangway. He would follow up behind them both.

As he stepped onto the foot of the gangway he began to feel faint and his legs began to buckle under him. Clutching his Gladstone bag in one hand, he held on to the rail of the gangway as tightly as he could with the other hand to prevent himself from collapsing. This feeling was followed by waves of what only could be described as panic and fear, much the same as his experience in Capetown when he had been at the shipping office. Perspiration was breaking out on his brow as he used all his remaining strength to remain on his feet. Elizabeth, turning around from her position half way up the gangway, called back to him, 'What on earth's the matter Tom?'. Both women now started back down the gangway towards him, with Elizabeth saying loudly and nervously, 'You're shaking, Tom!'. And then, 'What's come over you?'. Thomas, still holding onto the handrail as for dear life, replied in a trembling voice, 'It's all right, my dear. Don't concern yourself. I shall be all right in a minute'. Elizabeth, gaining some control, said to him a little more quietly, 'You're so pale, Tom. What is it?'. Beginning to regain his composure, he replied, 'I don't know, my dear. I think I'm over it now. Let's go on board'. Both women, very worried about Thomas, reluctantly turned and continued up the gangway. Thomas slowly came up behind them.

Once on board, they immediately took in the plush red carpeting and the beautiful wood panelling in the entrance lobby. Crossing over to the Purser's office, Thomas, now feeling somewhat recovered, deposited his Gladstone bag there. They were assigned a steward who would show them to their cabins, which would be on

E deck. 'This way, if you will follow me, sir', said the steward, smartly dressed in his white tunic with epaulettes, blue trousers and shiny black shoes. They fell in behind him as they went along the passageway with its varnished handrails and oak panelling. The smell of newness was everywhere. They went down two flights of stairs to arrive on E deck and, after a short walk along the passageway, arrived outside of the ladies' cabin.

On opening the cabin door for them, the steward then led Thomas a few doors further along, to his two-berth cabin, which he would be sharing with another gentleman. Their baggage arrived soon after and was placed in the centre of the cabin as they looked around at their surroundings. They were well pleased with the accommodation with one bunk above the other, made up with big white pillows, crispy white sheets and decorative counterpanes with the White Star logo in the centre. The floor was beautifully carpeted and there were two comfortable chairs, a wash stand and mirror, fluffy white towels, water jugs and glasses. The bunks had curtains that could be drawn right across and there were matching neat little curtains at the porthole. Thomas, on returning from his own cabin, which was identical to theirs, said, as he spread his arms out in an expansive gesture, 'Well, ladies. What do you think?'. Elizabeth replied, 'It's as good as they said it would be. I'm very impressed with the cabin and I must say, it's as good as first class on the Union Castle Line'. Edith, stepping up a few steps on the varnished bunk ladder and inspecting the upper berth, said to her mother, 'I'm for the top bunk, mother!'. Elizabeth laughed, saying to her daughter, 'You're welcome to it, my dear. If I fall out of bed I don't want far to fall!'. Edith, laughing along with her mother, jumped back down on the floor.

Elizabeth, turning to her husband, said in a more serious tone, 'Are you feeling better after that turn you had just now, Tom?'. 'Yes much', was his reply and then he went on thoughtfully, 'I just don't understand it. I felt fine up until then'. And then chuckling, 'It's almost as though I should have remained on the dockside. Let's forget it. I'm feeling fine now'.

They decided to go up on deck and look the ship over, leaving their baggage unpacked in the middle of the cabin. There would be plenty of time for that but right now there was much to see of this wonderful vessel. Making their way up to the open decks, they passed many passengers in the passageways, sorting out their luggage and being directed to their cabins with stewards fussing about them. After going along passageways and up several flights of stairs, they arrived on the second class promenade deck and strolled along with other groups of people. They went to the ship's rail and looked down on the dockside far below them with throngs of people milling about, and cranes swinging their cargoes into the ship's holds. Edith, standing back a bit and appearing somewhat apprehensive about getting too close to the rail, said to her father, 'That's an awfully long way down'. Thomas replying, 'It certainly is and once you're on board, it gives you an idea of the size of this ship'. They continued their walk around the decks and, while up on the boat deck, noticed much more smoke coming out of the funnels, than what they had first seen from the train. There was also much steam coming out of the waste pipes at the tops of each funnel, an indication that the Titanic was preparing for sea.

Chapter Four
Titanic - Day one

Captain Smith would have arrived on board the Titanic around 7.30 a.m. after travelling from his home in Winn Road, Southampton. The crew were to be mustered at 8 a.m. and he would have a busy morning right up until sailing time at noon. There would be many comings and goings to his cabin with the Chief Engineer, port officials, including the Board of Trade and his senior officers. After muster that morning, a boat drill was carried out, in which just two boats were lowered into the water. These were manned by nine seamen each, who then rowed around the immediate dock area, testing some of the gear.

Coaling of the ship had been completed with coal being taken from the White Star ships, Oceanic and Majestic. Both ships had been laid up due to a national coal strike, which had ended just a few days ago. Down in the boiler rooms, firemen had been kept busy with a fire that had developed in no. 10 bunker and were hosing down and shovelling hot cinders away from the seat of the fire. Fires in the bunkers of coal-burning ships were not uncommon but could be difficult to control due to the restricted area in which the coal was kept. A close eye was kept on the situation with extra men being deployed to that section to keep things under control.

Able Seaman Fred Fleet was a paid lookout man, having served in that capacity when the ship came down from the builder's yard in Belfast. He had binoculars at that time but now discovered that they were missing from the box in the crow's nest since the ship had arrived in Southampton. He had approached the Second Officer for replacement binoculars but was told, along with the other lookout men , that none were available. The Board of Trade had issued certificates to say that the ship was in a seaworthy condition and that the 14 lifeboats could accommodate 910 persons, her two accident boats a further 80 persons, and the four collapsible boats another 188 persons, giving a total life-saving capacity of 1178 persons in all boats. With a total of over 2200 passengers and crew there was only life-saving equipment for just

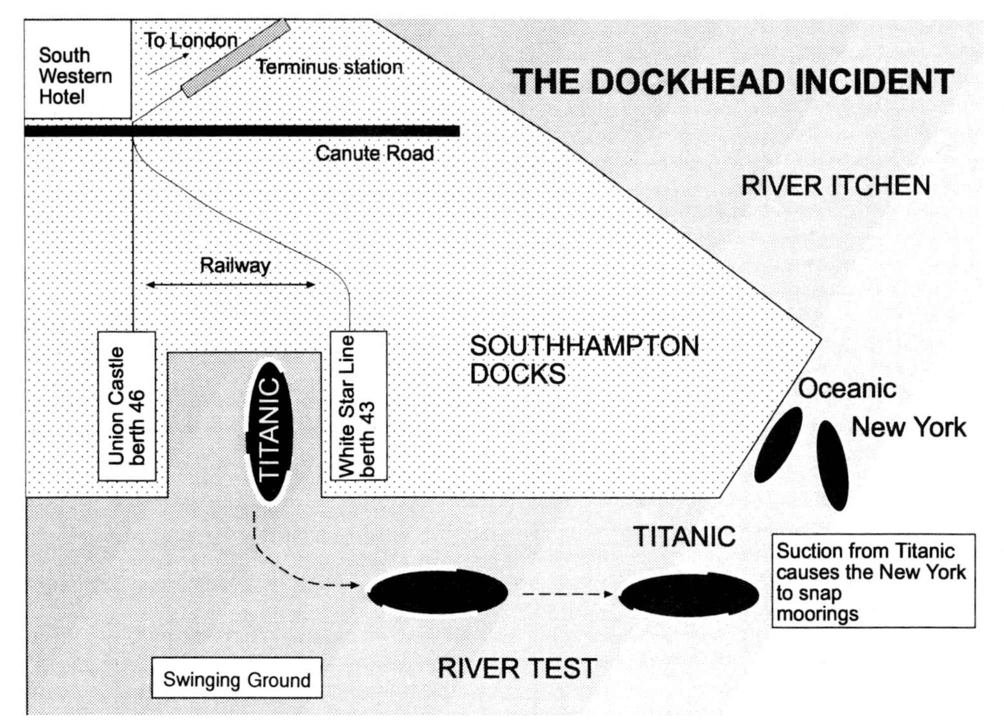

Above: The Dockhead Incident.

half of that number.

The Titanic was to sail across the Atlantic, after calling in at Cherbourg in France and Queenstown in Ireland. Throughout the morning the dockside became more crowded with dock workers, passengers and well wishers all jostling together. A carnival type atmosphere ensued as sailing time drew forever closer. The Browns continued their walk around the upper decks, pausing to look over the ship's rail from time to time to observe the activity below them on the dockside. Shore personnel were seen to be forever going up and down the three gangways, carrying packages, boxes, and flowers. There were still some third class passengers boarding the ship at the forward gangway, along with some crewmembers carrying their kit. There was an argument going on between some stokers and the Master at Arms at the foot of that gangway. He was trying to prevent them from boarding the vessel. Apparently, they had arrived late for their watch-keeping duties after a final drinking session in The Grapes, a public house ashore, and other unemployed stokers had taken their jobs on the dockside. They were extremely angry at the loss of their jobs but little did they know at the time, that their last drink ashore had probably saved their lives.

Shortly after this altercation, the last of the third class passengers was seen boarding the ship from this gangway. Accommodation here was mostly for single males as it was situated at this end of the ship. As the last of the emigrants struggled aboard with their suitcases and bundles, one was heard to say. 'It's going to be a bloody long walk getting to the women on this ship!'. Finally, a crane swung its jib around and a sling was attached to the gangway in readiness to lift it away as sailing time approached.

Thomas, along with his wife and daughter, continued to watch the activity below them when suddenly, there was an ear-shattering blast as the ship's whistle sounded. Passengers up on deck were caught by surprise, and ducking almost as one, quickly realised what it was, as they looked up at the massive funnels, laughing amongst themselves.

Up on the bridge, Captain Smith ordered the Chief Officer to have the forward gangway removed and the bosun called the men to stations. Within ten minutes of the ship's whistle echoing around the port of Southampton, three tugs slowly arrived off berth 43 in readiness to take up their towing positions. The choice of pilot was Captain Bowyer, one of a long line of Bowyers who still pilot ships out of Southampton to this very day. He arrived on the bridge, accompanied by a junior officer, and shook Captain Smith's hand saying, 'Good morning, Captain. How was your run down from Belfast?'. 'Fine,' replied the captain, and then added, 'She did all that was asked of her and briefly touched 24 knots'. Then he added, 'We don't intend to push her on this voyage but if the weather is on our side, she could do well'.

The pilot, nodding his head in an understanding way, walked over to the binnacle and checked the reading on the compass to a fixed marker ashore. The Titanic sailed from Southampton 15 minutes late due to the late arrival of the first class boat train. As the ship's moorings were being let go, the tugs Neptune, Vulcan and Hector began to pull her off the quay, the gap slowly widening between ship and shore. Streamers were being stretched to their limit as passengers threw flowers to those on the quayside, amid shouts and waving as the ship's orchestra continued to play lively music. Thomas, Elizabeth and Edith said little, but waved, along with everyone else, just enjoying the wonderful atmosphere, as the ship slowly moved away from berth 43. Once clear of the dockside, the ship started gently to go astern, the people ashore still waving and walking to keep pace with her. Out of the dock basin, the Titanic's stern was pulled around upstream until she was facing seaward. The passengers on the stern would have noticed considerable turbulence down in the water as her three mighty bronze propellers churned up the water beneath them. The tugs were let go and pulled away. The people on the dockside were still waving, although it was becoming more difficult to make out their faces.

As the Titanic gathered way, just ahead of her there were two ships, the Oceanic and the New York, moored together, side by side on a berth known as Dock Head. The New York, being the outboard vessel, snapped her moorings due to the suction from the Titanic and swung out in front of her. On the bridge, Captain Smith immediately ordered all three engines full astern in order to prevent a collision and, with the assistance of the tug Vulcan, avoided what may well have been a serious incident.

Down on the second class promenade deck, the Browns had witnessed this near collision and Thomas, again looking quite pale and a little shaky, said to his wife, 'I don't like it! This is a bad omen'. Edith, turning to look at Thomas inquired, 'What do you mean father?'. Elizabeth, once again showing concern for her husband and noticing the perspiration forming on his brow, said to her daughter, 'Your father thinks its a sign of bad luck, but don't worry about it, my dear, it's only an old sailors' superstition'. Thomas, still appearing a bit shaken, continued to stare at the New York as she was towed out of danger by the Vulcan. He finally said to his wife, 'I hope you're right, my dear'. Once the ship was well clear of the Titanic, Captain Smith gave the order of half ahead on all engines again, as she started to move forward, heading down Southampton Water towards the Solent.

The Titanic rounded the West Brambles Bank off Cowes, the world famous yachting centre on the Isle of Wight and, gathering speed, headed for the Nab Tower where the pilot would disembark. On occasions when the sea was too rough for the pilot to leave a vessel, he would stay on board and disembark at Cherbourg. On this day, however, 10 April 1912, the weather was good and the sea calm. The pilot left as usual, as Britain continued to enjoy one of the mildest winters for decades. Many of the passengers, having been on deck slowly watching the scenery passing by, were now seated in their respective dining saloons, enjoying lunch, their first meal of the voyage.

In the second class dining saloon, the Browns had the Reverend Earnest Carter and his wife, Lillian as dining companions and soon struck up a conversation with them as they ate their meal. 'What brings you and your good lady onto a wonderful ship like this, Reverend?' asked Thomas. 'To us, this is a trip of a lifetime', replied Earnest Carter emphatically to his question. He then went on, 'We come from a relatively small parish and have been saving our pennies for years to just once visit America'. Turning to his wife, he added, 'It's been your dream for years, hasn't it Lillian?'. 'Oh yes!' replied Mrs Carter, 'And what better way to go than on a beautiful ship such as this?'. 'Yes, quite so,' said Elizabeth, joining in and then inquiring, 'Will you be staying in America long?'. 'Not long,' replied Lillian, with a smile, 'Earnest won't leave his beloved parish for long'. The Reverend Carter looked knowingly at his wife and added, 'You know as well as I do that there is still much to be done in the parish'. Lillian replied, 'Yes, that's true, but I think they will survive without you for a spell'. Turning his gaze on Thomas he asked, 'Would you be on a business trip, may I ask?'. 'You could say that,' replied Thomas, 'I'm hoping to start up a hotel business in Seattle if all goes well'. 'Oh that's splendid!' replied Earnest Carter enthusiastically, 'I wish you and your family well'.

At 2 p.m. the pilot cutter drew alongside to let the pilot off and, once clear, the captain ordered all engines full ahead as the Titanic headed for Cherbourg. The total number of passengers who boarded the Titanic in Southampton was 190 first class, 230 second class and 500 third class, including a crew of almost 900. Of that number, there were 20 passengers who had joined the ship, just to do a trip across the English Channel and they would be disembarking at Cherbourg.

After a wonderful lunch in the dining saloon, which gave them all a foretaste of the superb cuisine they could expect on this voyage, the Browns set off on further walks around the ship. They visited the library with its beautiful oak panelling, rows of well stocked book cases, comfortable armchairs and attractive standard lamps placed around the room. Elizabeth and Edith were avid readers and were delighted with the range of books, knowing they would be spending many pleasant hours here throughout the voyage.

Thomas was well pleased with the smoking room with its sycamore panelling and green leather padded chairs. There were card tables and a bar at one end and it had the atmosphere of a gentleman's club. They went back up on deck but didn't stay for long as they found it too cold and breezy as the ship now doing over 20 knots and creating her own wind as she ploughed across the channel. During this short voyage across the English Channel, they enjoyed afternoon tea and cakes in one of the lounges. Edith, with her sweet tooth, was tucking in to a huge sponge cake and said to Elizabeth, 'I think I'm going to enjoy this trip, mother'. Elizabeth laughingly replied, 'I don't know where you put it all after the lunch you've just had!'.

The Titanic arrived outside Cherbourg at 6.30 p.m. and dropped anchor in the harbour. Passengers were to be brought out to the ship on two tenders. These two ferries were named Traffic and Nomadic and were built by Harland and Wolf in Belfast, primarily for this type of work in Cherbourg. Many passengers began to gather on deck to watch the arrival of these two tenders, the first one alongside bringing the first class passengers and the other tender with second and third class passengers on board. Among the 142 first class passengers boarding from the tender, there were many well known wealthy people of that time. A further 30 second class and just on 100 third class passengers also boarded from the second tender. In addition to their baggage there was also a great quantity of mail to be loaded and, once on board, it was taken straight to the mailroom for sorting.

At 8 p.m. Captain Smith gave the order to raise the anchor as the tenders pulled away from the ship. Once clear, they gave the Titanic three toots on their whistles to wish the ship 'Bon Voyage'. The liner responded with three thunderous blasts from her own whistles, which must have been heard all over Cherbourg. Once the anchor was weighed, the Titanic, with her deck lights blazing and pinhole lights showing from her portholes, slowly turned away from Cherbourg and headed into the English Channel. With her four massive funnels floodlit, she would have made a spectacular sight to those onlookers ashore.

Of the rich and famous on board, there was Isodor Straus and his wife Ida, owners of the well known Macy's department stores in America. They always travelled abroad with her maid and his valet. There was John Jacob Astor with his young wife Madeleine, just half his age and Bruce Ismay, the White Star Line's managing director who was also occupying one of the staterooms, and travelling with his valet and secretary. Thomas Andrews, the ship's designer was also in a first class cabin although this would be a working voyage for him. Also on this voyage were several shipyard technicians, brought along to iron out any of the teething problems that sometimes occur on maiden voyages. These men had been with her when her keel was laid and knew practically every rivet that had gone into her construction. They had been there at the start and had helped to build her, knew her as a 'good job' and were proud to be sailing in her on her maiden voyage.

In the third class, many of the emigrants that had boarded at Cherbourg had travelled long distances through France and Eastern Europe and were glad of a good meal and some well earned sleep. In the second class library, Edith and her mother were feeling the effects of a very long day and had decided to turn in for the night. They were escorted to their cabin by Thomas, who on kissing them both at their door said, 'Goodnight, my dears. Sleep well. I shall see you in the morning'. Closing the door behind them, he went up to the smoking room for a nightcap before finally turning in himself.

The Titanic steamed westward throughout the night, heading for Queenstown in Southern Ireland. The fire in no. 10 bunker was still burning. The stokers had still not been able to put it out despite their efforts.

R.M.S. "TITANIC"

APRIL 14, 1912.

LUNCHEON.

CONSOMMÉ FERMIER   COCKIE LEEKIE

FILLETS OF BRILL

EGG À L'ARGENTEUIL

CHICKEN À LA MARYLAND

CORNED BEEF VEGETABLES, DUMPLINGS

FROM THE GRILL.

GRILLED MUTTON CHOPS

MASHED, FRIED & BAKED JACKET POTATOES

CUSTARD PUDDING

APPLE MERINGUE   PASTRY

BUFFET.

SALMON MAYONNAISE   POTTED SHRIMPS

NORWEGIAN ANCHOVIES   SOUSED HERRINGS

PLAIN & SMOKED SARDINES

ROAST BEEF

ROUND OF SPICED BEEF

VEAL & HAM PIE

VIRGINIA & CUMBERLAND HAM

BOLOGNA SAUSAGE   BRAWN

GALANTINE OF CHICKEN

CORNED OX TONGUE

LETTUCE   BEETROOT   TOMATOES

CHEESE.

CHESHIRE, STILTON, GORGONZOLA, EDAM,
ÇAMEMBERT, ROQUEFORT, ST. IVEL.
CHEDDAR

Iced draught Munich Lager Beer 3d. & 6d. a Tankard.

Lunch menu from the Titanic.

Chapter Five

Titanic - Day two

At daybreak on 11 April the sea was calm and, generally, the weather was still mild for the time of the year. During the night the Titanic had steamed some 240 nautical miles, had rounded Lands End on the south-western most point of the British Isles, and had entered St Georges Channel. At 11.30 a.m. she had arrived at Queenstown and dropped anchor just off of Roches Point. For those passengers with their accommodation in the third class forward compartments, the dropping of the anchor would be an experience many of them were not likely to forget. There would have been a thunderous roar, as the huge links of the anchor chain would have scraped and banged up the spurling pipe from the chain locker below. There would have been great rattling noises as the chain raced around the capstan up on deck and crashed down the awes pipe, following the huge anchor into the sea. It would leave them in little doubt as to why the fares for travelling in this part of the ship were the cheapest on board.

Soon after dropping the anchor, two tenders could be seen coming out of the harbour and heading towards the Titanic. As they drew closer it could be seen that they were paddle steamers and, once they were almost alongside, their names could be made out. They were appropriately called Ireland and America. Among the crowd that gathered up on deck to watch these two vessels draw alongside were the Carters and the Browns. Leaning over the side, the Reverend Carter said to Thomas, 'They look so small up against the Titanic'. Thomas replied, 'They certainly do. It looks as though there is quite a bit of mail to come aboard'. After securing their lines, a somewhat rickety gangway was hoisted up to the Titanic's shell doors, which were situated about four meters above the top deck of the tenders.

Once secured, several port officials boarded, followed soon after by the passengers and their baggage. Several traders had come out with the tenders and were now on board up on the second class promenade deck, displaying their wares and beautiful Irish linens. There was a young fiddler, playing Irish jigs with his open cap lying on the deck at his feet. If the number of coins was anything to go by, his playing was well appreciated by the onlookers. Thomas purchased a set of lace handkerchiefs for his wife and daughter, along with some other items and also a beautiful tablecloth of the best Irish linen. He presented it to Elizabeth saying, 'This is to grace our table, when we get one to put it on'.

During the Titanic's brief stay at Queenstown, she had taken on a further 110 third class passengers, six second class passengers and 1400 sacks of mail. It was discovered that, while the ship was at Queenstown, one of the stokers had decided that he wasn't happy with the Titanic and jumped ship, stowing away on one of the tenders. Of the seven passengers disembarking at Queenstown, one of them was a keen photographer and, on leaving the Titanic, took a picture of Captain Smith looking down from the bridge, probably the last picture ever taken of him. At 1 p.m. all the passengers were on board with the mail having been taken to the mailroom for sorting.

Nearly all of the passengers were in their dining saloons being served lunch, with just a few remaining on deck, watching the tenders leave. Up in the bows the winch gear could be heard as the anchor was raised and, shortly afterwards, the Titanic turned her head seaward. Once clear of the liner, the tenders gave the customary three toots on their whistles again to wish all of those on board a good trip. Again the ship responded with three thunderous blasts from her own whistles, as her bow swung westward. The weather was still fine although becoming chilly as the ship slowly gathered speed and headed for the North Atlantic. As lunch progressed, not much would have been heard in the dining saloons other than the usual clatter of cutlery and crockery and the murmurs of conversations. It, therefore, came as a bit of a surprise to many, when venturing up on deck after their meal, to find the ship well under way and out to sea.

Edith and her father decided to go up on the enclosed promenade deck after their meal, while Elizabeth preferred to go below for a nap in her cabin. Edith, holding onto her father's arm as they strolled around the deck, said to him, 'Have you ever met Aunt Josephine in Seattle father?'. Her father replied, 'No, I haven't as a matter of fact, my dear, but I' m really looking forward to getting there and meeting new friends'. Turning to look at his daughter as they continued their walk, he asked,

'How about you? Are you looking forward to your new life in Seattle?'. Edith replied, a little uncertainly, 'I am, but I don't really know what to expect other than the little bits that you and mother have told me'. Stopping their walk, they went over to the ship's rail and looked at the beautiful green hills along the Irish coastline. Thomas said, 'If things work out, we will all have a good future to look forward to but, if not, I shall take you and your mother back to South Africa where we shall pick up where we left off'. He then finally added, 'It will be fine, my dear. Just you wait and see'. At the stern of the ship, several passengers could be seen looking back at the slowly disappearing Irish coast, a coastline that many of them would never see again.

In the first class accommodation, the rich and the famous were preparing to go down for cocktails and then, afterwards, to the dining saloon for dinner. Bruce Ismay was in his stateroom with Thomas Andrews discussing the ship's performance since leaving Southampton. Both men were apparently well pleased with the way she was behaving. Thomas Brown was in the smoking room, enjoying a drink while he waited for the ladies to dress, before escorting them down to the dining saloon.

Down in the engine room, engineers were sipping tea from mugs, walking around the machinery, checking temperatures, pressures gauges and moving parts. In the boiler rooms it was sweat and toil all the way with firemen stripped to the waist, shovelling never-ending quantities of coal into the roaring fires. By the time the Titanic would have reached New York, these men would have shovelled some 3000 tons of coal into her hungry furnaces.

After dinner that evening, many passengers retired to the lounges to relax after being pampered for nearly two hours in the dining saloons. It was here that shipboard gossip was passed around and one would quickly find out who was who on board. There would also be many exaggerated tales about the wonderful ship on which they were travelling, the things that were available on board, and the exquisite catering, especially in the first class dining saloon and Verandah Grill Restaurant. They would talk about the Countess of Rothes, the Astors, the Straus family, and rich American women with their funny little dogs. Everyone that was anyone would come under the microscope on this great floating city and, of course, it was a pleasant way to pass away the time. There were many business people on board and, no doubt, one or two deals would be struck before arriving in New York.

Others that frequently travelled on these great transatlantic liners were professional gamblers, although the White Star Line was not the only carrier that had that problem.

The Titanic ploughed through the sea, white foam lit up by the ship's lights being forced away from the ship's side, as she headed into the night. Ahead of her, just blackness, with America still a long way away. Behind her, one or two solitary lights on the horizon. For those on board, a very uncertain future, for most, no future at all.

Chapter Six

Titanic - Day three

It was the morning of Friday, 12 April. Edith lying in her top bunk had been awake for some time thinking about Seattle and what it would be like living there, not knowing anyone. Lying there quietly she could hear from deep down inside the ship the distant throb of the engines and the faint whine of electric motors. She finally sat up, pulled her bunk curtains apart and, placing her feet on the bunk ladder, turned and stepped down to the cabin floor. At the same time, her mother in the lower berth, pulled her curtains apart and greeted her daughter. Edith, crossing the cabin floor to the porthole, told her mother that she had slept like a log and that she hadn't remembered a thing after putting my head on the pillow last night. 'It must be the sea air,' replied Elizabeth. And then she added, 'I haven't slept like I did last night for ages'.

Edith, looking out of the porthole, could see that it was the start of another nice day, with the sea calm and the sun trying to break through the grey early morning cloud. Turning away from the porthole, she said to her mother, 'It looks like another nice day out there, mother'. Elizabeth, getting out of her bunk, replied, 'That's good'. She slid her feet into a pair of slippers and added, 'We'd better get dressed before your father arrives to take us to breakfast'. Thomas tapped the door shortly afterwards and asked them whether they were ready for breakfast. Elizabeth said that as soon as Edith has finished brushing her hair they would be ready. Edith announced, 'I'm ready and I'm starving!'. Her mother gave a short laugh and added, 'You always are. Perhaps that's the sea air as well'.

On entering the dining saloon, they met the Carters who had arrived at the same time and, after exchanging the usual pleasantries, sat down to examine the breakfast menu. Some of the choices on offer, apart from a wide range of cereals and fruit juice, were sauteed kidneys, eggs and bacon, sausages, grilled tomatoes and fried bread. There was also the American dish pancakes with honey or maple syrup.

During the meal the Reverend Carter asked Thomas, 'May I ask which denomination you belong to?'. Thomas replied, 'Church of England,' and then pushing a piece of sausage around his plate before popping it in his mouth, added, 'We had our own pew in Capetown Cathedral and rarely missed a Sunday service'. The Reverend Carter then went on, 'I understand the Purser will be taking the Sunday service in the library'. He then concluded, 'Perhaps I should contact him and offer my services for the evening session'.

After breakfast, Edith and her mother decided to go to the library to take advantage of some of the wonderful books they had there and to read the newspapers that had come aboard at Queenstown. Thomas, on the other hand, decided to take a brisk walk around the boat deck to work off the large breakfast he had just eaten. Once on the upper decks, he noticed that it was colder than the day before but considered that to be normal now that they were further out to sea and well away from land. As he continued along the boat deck, he noticed a ship's officer climbing down from the ship's master compass platform, which was situated between the second and third funnels. Thomas decided this to be an opportune moment to inquire about the ship's arrival in New York.

'Good morning, sir,' greeted Thomas as the officer walked towards him. 'A very good morning to you, sir,' came the crisp reply, 'I trust you're enjoying the voyage?'. 'Oh yes! Very much so,' replied Thomas, who then added, 'She's a fine ship'. He then inquired whether the ship was likely to break any records this trip. The officer, replying carefully, said that that would be up to the Captain and Chief Engineer if they saw fit. He said, however, that it was not company policy to drive ships too hard on their maiden voyages. He then said with a quick short laugh, 'Better to play safe, and arrive on time, than not to arrive at all!'. Thomas, giving one of his well known little chuckles, replied, 'One couldn't ask for more'. He then wished the officer a pleasant day and continued on his walk around the boat deck.

Edith and her mother were well engrossed in their reading when another woman passenger came into the library and started up a conversation with Elizabeth. Edith, overhearing the conversation, heard the woman say, 'Do you know, there's something about this ship that I find very unsettling'. Elizabeth, quite a nervous person at the best of times, looked at her anxiously and asked, 'In what way?'. The woman replied, 'Quite frankly, I can't put my finger on it, but when we were in

Queenstown, I wanted my husband to cancel the voyage and get me off'. Edith looked up from the book she was reading and studied the woman's face. She thought that she did indeed look a like bundle of nerves. The woman went on, 'My husband and I have made several trips across the Atlantic over the years and, although I'm not keen on sea travel, I usually settle down after the first day or two'. She went on, 'Since I've been on this ship, I haven't slept a wink and I just feel uneasy the whole time although, one must admit, she's a beautiful ship for all of that'. Elizabeth replied, 'It's most extraordinary. I do hope you're able to settle as the trip goes on'. The woman finally added, 'I hope so. I could do with a good night's sleep, I know that'.

The Purser's office is the one place on a passenger ship where everyone visits during the voyage, as all passenger requirements are controlled from there. Apart from offering a banking service on board it is also the information centre for the entire vessel. It was here that Thomas arrived, just after midday, to study the ship's daily run details, and to observe the chart, enclosed in a glass case on one of the panelled walls in the foyer. The chart showed the whole of the North Atlantic from the west coast of England right across to the eastern seaboard of North America.

For navigational purposes the ship's day begins and ends at noon and soon after the ship's position is taken, details of speed, etc. are displayed for passengers' convenience. The ship's position is marked by a red button and all other details are inserted at the bottom of the glass case on a piece of paper brought down from the bridge. A daily sweepstake was run on this information with passengers betting on the exact mileage covered each day, with the person having the closest estimate being the outright winner.

Thomas liked a flutter but didn't think his chances would bear much fruit on this day's run. The Titanic had logged 385 nautical miles since leaving Queenstown, which was well short of the expected daily mileage. Taking the betting slip out of his pocket he noticed that he was about 50 miles out but that was due to the ship travelling for only 22 hours since leaving Queenstown. Tomorrow should be interesting, he thought as she would have steamed for 24 hours without interruption and there will be a more realistic figure on her mileage. The slip of paper sent down from the bridge showed that her average speed was only just over 17 knots and everyone knew she could do better than that.

In the lounges there was talk that the ship might reach New York on Tuesday night, 16 April, instead of 17 as scheduled. Passengers would still have to remain on board until the morning. This would mean, however, that her estimated time of arrival would be some 12 hours sooner than advertised, giving the White Star Line the edge on all other North Atlantic carriers. This of course would do wonders for the mail contract and the company's prestige internationally. All of this being achieved on a brand new liner on her maiden voyage was a real possibility, and with the excellent unseasonable weather to help her along, it was no doubt very tempting to 'go for it'.

There was also talk in the lounges about vibration, which could now be felt down in the cabins for the first time since the start of the voyage. This was particularly more noticeable on the lower decks towards the after end of the ship. It was well known by marine engineers that these big ships needed a day or two to settle down to reach their cruising speeds, and weather permitting, the Titanic would improve each day.

Relaxing in deckchairs on the enclosed promenade deck, Edith commented to her mother on how young some of the bellboys looked. Elizabeth, realising that her daughter was now of an age where she would be noticing boys more, answered her by saying, 'Yes, they are very young looking'. And then she went on, 'Some of them look as though they should be back home with their mothers'. Thomas joined in by saying, 'They sign them on at the age of 14, much the same as the hotel industry ashore'. Elizabeth added, 'Perhaps it's the only way some of the poor little beggars will ever see the world'. Edith, rising out of her deckchair, said to her parents, 'Would you mind if I went to the library?'. Elizabeth replied that it was fine and said they would catch up with her later. After she had left, Thomas said to his wife, 'It's a pity there aren't any other young people her age in the second class. She seems quite lonely at times'. Elizabeth replied, 'Yes, I agree,' and then added, 'I've been thinking about that lately, but the voyage isn't very long and, once we get to Seattle, let's hope she'll meet others her own age'.

After chatting between themselves for some time, they began to feel chilly and decided to go into the lounge for afternoon tea. It was here that they took up conversation with another middle-aged couple that they had spoken to earlier in the voyage. After the usual small talk on their meeting, Mr Jones then went on, 'Did you know that since leaving Southampton, there's been a fire raging down in the stokehole and up to this moment in time, they are still unable to put it out?'. This was the last thing Thomas wanted to hear, and turning to Elizabeth at his side, noticed that this revelation wasn't doing her nerves any good. Mr Jones continued, 'Our saloon steward has a friend who is a stoker on board, and he told him that they are still deploying extra men down there to try and keep it under control'. Thomas decided to play it down a bit by saying, 'I'm sure it's under control, besides, ship's being what they are for gossip, it's fairly certain that more people would have heard about it by now'. Mr Jones, not to be deterred, went on, 'That may be so, but it doesn't fill one with much confidence in the White Star Line, does it?'. His wife, a huge woman, nodded at every word her husband said, looking first at Thomas, then at Elizabeth and back to her husband. Thomas, realising a rapid escape was necessary, said to them, 'I've just remembered, we must take our leave of you, our daughter is expecting us up in the library'. Once outside the lounge, Thomas said to his wife, 'I think we can go without tea for the moment, my dear and take it later'.

During dinner that evening at the captain's table, Bruce Ismay was overheard asking Captain Smith if the extra boilers had yet been fired up. The captain was heard to reply, 'I don't feel it's necessary at the present time, Mr Ismay. She's making good headway and can well sustain her speed as things are, especially with these good weather conditions'. Ismay replied, 'Yes, that may be so, Captain but if we could fire up those spare boilers she could well beat the Olympic's time to New York'.

That evening after retiring to their cabin, Elizabeth and Edith noticed quite a bit of vibration around the cabin for the first time. A slight rattle from the door handle now and then, the clink of the glasses on the washstand and the occasional creak from the wood panelling were all sounds they had not noticed before on the voyage. Edith, after undressing and slipping on her nightgown, climbed the small ladder to her upper berth, got under the bedclothes, said goodnight to her mother, drew her curtains and turned out her bunk light. Elizabeth, sitting on the edge of her bunk in her nightclothes, listened to the noises around the cabin and the distant throb of the ship's engines. Her thoughts turned to the conversation earlier in the day with Mr Jones about the fire in the stoke hole and she wondered if there was any truth in such a story. She remembered what Thomas had said about the matter and decided that he made more sense. Finally, getting under the bedclothes, she drew her curtains and, on turning out her light, asked Edith if she was warm enough. There was no reply. Edith had fallen into a deep contented sleep.

In third class, Kate O' Mara was sharing a four-berth cabin with three other single women. She was travelling with her father, after leaving their tied cottage on a small farm near Limerick in Ireland, to join her uncle and his wife in Brooklyn. Her mother had died two years previously and since then her uncle had written to them repeatedly to persuade them to come out to America to start a new life. At 18 years of age, Kate was a woman of rare beauty, with her long black shoulder-length hair and a beautiful complexion that comes with spending all of one's life on a farm. She was of medium height with firm breasts and shapely legs. Her most outstanding features were her beautiful deep blue eyes and soft lips that could cause any man's heart to miss a beat.

Her father was a powerfully built farm labourer who, over these past few years, had spent a great deal of time, keeping the local lads away from his daughter. Kate O' Mara, lying on her top bunk, stared at the white paintwork and the rows of rivets several feet above her head. She was thinking about the good-looking man who hadn't taken his eyes off her all night. There had been quite a large number of people in the social area this evening, laughing and drinking with some taking to the floor as a man played his fiddle, another used an upturned wash tub as a drum and a third clacked away with a set of spoons. The good-looking man had excited her, but she knew that her father was keeping an eye on her, so had to behave as though she wasn't taking any notice.

In third class at the other end of the ship, Patrick Doyle was preparing to turn in for the night in his six-berth cabin. He was having a bit of a laugh with his cabin mate, Frank Denton, who was saying to him, 'I notice you had your eye on that little dark-haired beauty tonight?'. 'Aye', replied Patrick and he went on, 'Next time it will be more than just having my eye on her, and that's a promise!'. Frank laughing and gently slapping his friend on the shoulder continued, 'You'll have to get past the big guy first who, I shouldn't wonder, looks as though he is her father'. Patrick, laughing along with his friend, went on, 'Once he knows what a fine upstanding man I am, he'll be butter in my hands'. Frank, laughing even louder, went on, 'Once he gets to know you, you'll be pulp in his hands!'. Patrick, still laughing, assured his friend that love would find a way. Frank enjoying this banter with his friend asked whether Patrick had noticed the size of the man. He commented on his shoulders which he said were 'like a barn door' and his 'hands like shovels that would swat you like a fly if you got too close'. Patrick, laughing even louder, replied that in his opinion the woman was crazy about him and anyone could see that!

With that one of the occupants across the other side of the cabin wrenched his bunk curtain aside and shouted, 'Why don't you two bloody love birds shut your gobs and let us all get some sleep!'. Patrick, turning to face him, said in a pacifying tone, 'Come now. 'Tis such a small world that we are living in at the moment, there really isn't any room for such anger and we should all get along together'. The occupant, peering at them both with bloodshot eyes, made a rude sign and shut them out of view. Both men looked at each other, trying their hardest to stifle their laughter, as they prepared to get into their bunks. With the vibration being felt more in their cabin now, Frank finally said to his friend, 'She's rattling well tonight, Patrick!'.

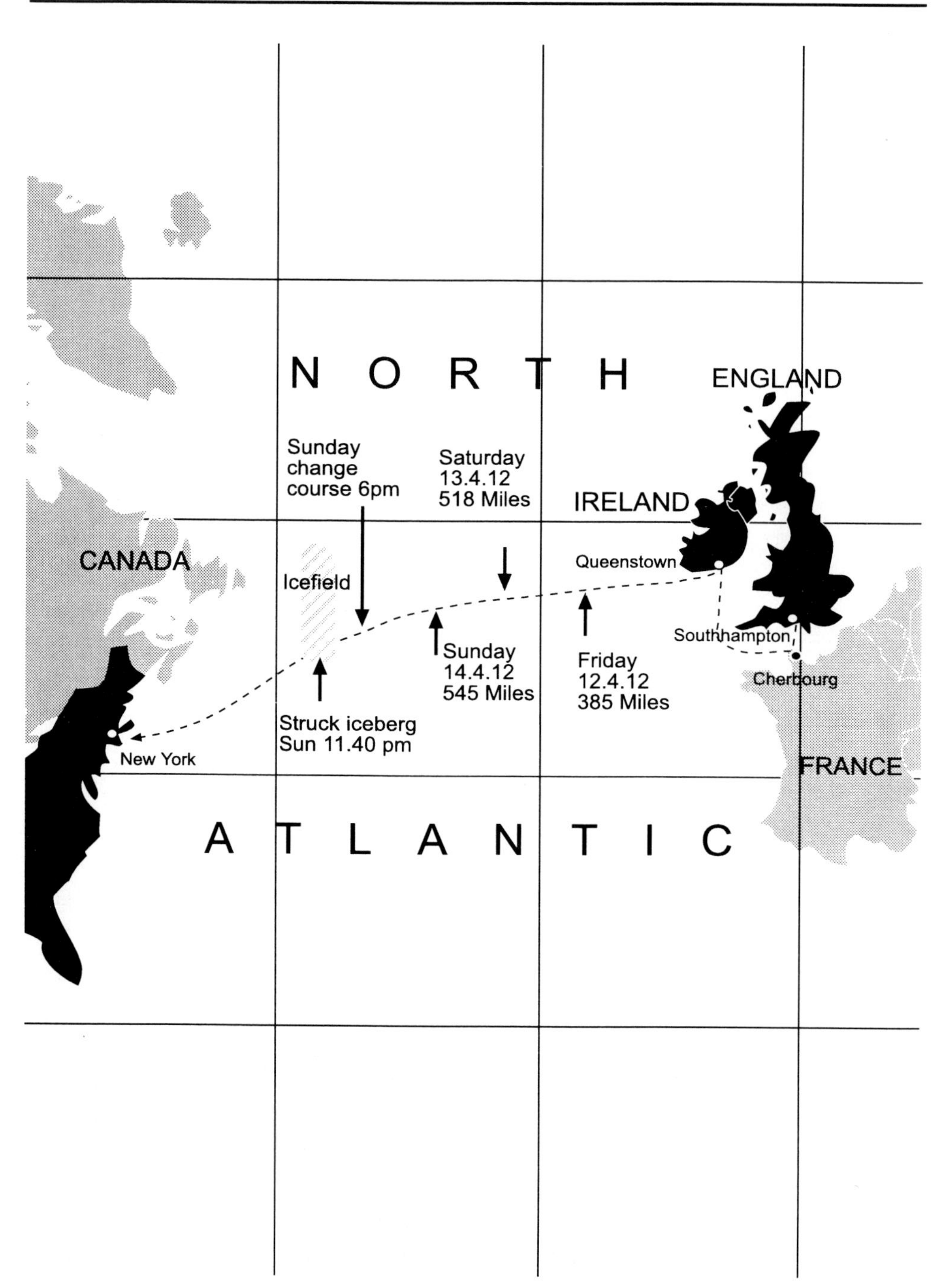

Illustration of the Titanic's voyage.

Chapter Seven

Titanic - Day four

It was Saturday, 13 April. The weather continued to be unusually fine for the North Atlantic at this time of the year. Captain Smith arrived in the wheelhouse just as the watch was changing over and made his way into the chartroom. On entering, he noticed his Chief Officer leaning over a chart on the chart table and made his way towards him saying, 'Good morning, Chief. How's she doing?'. The officer straightened up and turning towards his commander, replied, 'Good morning, sir'. Turning back to the chart before him, he placed his finger on a pencil cross he had just marked off and said, 'We've just worked out our position to be here at 0800 hours'. He then went on to say that he estimated the speed to be 21 knots and said there had been a noticeable drop in air and sea temperatures. He said that the second engineer has advised him that the fire in no. 10 bunker was just about out, but they would continue to monitor the situation and would confirm later this morning. The captain left the chartroom asking to be informed if anything untoward cropped up.

The ship's post office and mailrooms were situated well down at waterline level on G-deck. The postal workers down there had a mammoth task ahead of them, sorting mail from the hundreds of huge sacks, in readiness for arrival in New York. This was just another service White Star were offering and mail contracts were lucrative. They had already sorted the mail and had it ready for dispatch at the port of destination. The mail sorters were on shift work throughout the voyage, bringing up the sacks of mail from the mailrooms below and then sorting the mail into pigeonholes. Regardless to the amount of mail on board, the job had to be completed by the time of arrival on each voyage. They were not employed by the shipping company but by the General Post Office in England and it was considered to be a job with a difference to be able to visit America while doing a job as a mail sorter.

Captain Smith visited the second class deck at around 10 a.m. that morning on one of his public relations exercises for the White Star Line. It was company policy for the captain to visit all classes at least once on each voyage. As he walked along the enclosed promenade deck, stopping now and then to chat to passengers, he looked to be in a jovial mood. Smartly dressed in his full drape navy blue jacket, with medal ribbons across his chest and four gold rings around each cuff, he looked a fine figure of a man. Under his cap, with gold braid around its peak, was a kindly round face with his white beard, giving the impression of what everyone's favourite grandfather should look like. Along with his sharply creased navy blue trousers and black shiny shoes, he looked every bit the captain of the world's most famous liner.

As he continued his walk around the deck, he stopped and went over to the Browns sitting in deck chairs. Addressing them all he asked whether they were enjoying the voyage. Thomas replied for all of them when he said they were enjoying it very much. Captain Smith then turned his attention to Edith and smiling asked, 'And how about you, young lady?'. Edith, looking first at her mother and then back to the captain, replied, 'It's the best ship we've ever been on'. Captain Smith, letting out a laugh, said he was glad to hear it. Edith asked whether it was true that there were dogs on the ship. The captain replied that the ship had what was known as a 'dog deck', which was situated up by the funnels. There were kennels there where the dogs were looked after by one of the ship's butchers. Edith then asked, 'Have you got a dog, Captain?'. 'Yes,' came the reply and then he added with a laugh, 'Not on board the ship I hasten to add. He's back home in Southampton where he should be'. He then finally said, 'When I get back to Southampton after this voyage, I shall have more time to spend with him'. Thomas, changing the subject, then asked the captain whether the ship was running to schedule. Captain Smith replied that the ship was making good time with the excellent weather. He said they would reach New York by the time advertised. He then added that it was a pity that it had got colder but it's what you can expect in these waters at this time of the year. With that, he gave them a half salute and wished them a pleasant day.

On completing his goodwill tour of second class, Captain Smith returned to his cabin to be met by his chief engineer who wanted a word with him. Captain Smith sensed that it was something unusually important. The captain, standing by the doorway of his cabin, asked his chief to come in and take a seat. On entering the cabin, they both took a seat facing each other across the room with Captain Smith inquiring about the problem. The engineer replied that he had had a visit from Bruce

Ismay who had wanted to know how things were down below and, especially, how the boilers were standing up. Captain Smith leaned forward, listening intently to what his engineer was saying. After a pause, the chief went on to say that the ship was running well, with pressures and temperatures constant. The revs on all engines had increased slightly, but this was much as you would expect. The captain then asked what Ismay's response had been. The engineer recounted Ismay's response which was that he felt that, as the weather was on our side and she had plenty of extra coal in her bunkers, this presented a good opportunity to flash up the remaining boilers to see how she takes it.

Captain Smith became annoyed at this, not with his engineer, but with Ismay for going over his head in the running of the ship. The Titanic and everyone on board was his responsibility and if things went wrong, he would take full blame as the captain, which is what he would expect. He had, up to this point, operated the ship the way any ship's captain would on a maiden voyage and that was not to push her too hard and to keep to the company's advertised timetable. This would safeguard his position as master and would in itself be good enough for the company's prestige. Whichever way he looked at it though, Ismay was their employer and he and the chief engineer were now placed in a situation they should never be placed in. With his elbows on the arms of his chair and his hands clasped in front of him, the engineer looked directly at his captain and said, 'I'm reporting this to you now, sir as we are in the process of flashing up the remaining boilers'. The chief could see the annoyance on his captain's face as he leaned back and said in an almost resigned fashion, 'Very well, chief. Do what you have to do'.

At noon, the ship's position was fixed and it was shown that she had travelled some 518 nautical miles since noon the previous day, giving her an average speed of 21 knots. This was well within her service speed, which had been estimated by her designers to be around 24 knots. By late afternoon on this day, the Titanic had reached the halfway point across the Atlantic and was well on time for its arrival in New York.

One of Thomas's favourite pastimes whilst on board was to visit the smoking room where many of the gentlemen liked to have a chat and puff away on their pipes and cigars. Women never ventured there although there was nothing to say they shouldn't, it just wasn't the 'done thing'. They preferred instead to gather in the

Painting by David Haisman of the Titanic. Heading into the sunset on her last day afloat.

reading and writing rooms and talk about things that women liked to talk about. It was during this Saturday afternoon that one of the gentlemen talking to Thomas and the Reverend Carter mentioned that ice was of concern to some of the ship's navigating officers. This information came to him from one of the officers the previous day when the question of icebergs came up. The officer had told him that some of the ship's officers, who had crossed the North Atlantic many times before, were a bit concerned over the mild winter in the north. When the winters are mild, which is a rare event, much more ice breaks away in the spring, and drifts south with the currents. He assured him, however, that should such conditions present themselves, then they would not pose any threat to the safety of a ship like the Titanic, with her watertight compartments and sophisticated radio equipment.

In the first class lounge after dinner that evening, the ship's orchestra played dance music with many of the passengers taking to the floor. The opulence and luxury of the lounge, with its lavish decor and everyone beautifully dressed, gave it the appearance of the very best of hotels ashore. In the second class, part of the ship's orchestra was performing there as the passengers enjoyed card games, had drinks and chatted amongst themselves. A section of the floor had been cleared in the centre of the lounge for those wishing to dance. It was a pleasant atmosphere, Edith and her mother enjoying themselves as they watched the couples move around the floor.

Down in the third class section at the after end of the ship, they were also having a night of it with many of the men from the forward accommodation joining in. Patrick Doyle and his mate Frank Denton had arrived and taken a few turns on the floor with some of the colleens, when Patrick saw her, the beautiful Kate, arriving with the 'big guy'. Their eyes met and she briefly turned her gaze away with the faintest of smiles. Patrick decided to take the bull by the horns and went over to ask her to dance. Her father gave Patrick a hard look as if to say, 'Behave or else!' as she replied in her soft Irish brogue, 'Yes, I would like to'. Then turning with a cheeky look, she said to her father, half smiling, 'You can take that look off of your face as well!'.

TRIPLE SCREW STEAMER "TITANIC."

2ND CLASS

APRIL 14, 1912.

DINNER.

CONSOMME TAPIOCA

BAKED HADDOCK, SHARP SAUCE

CURRIED CHICKEN & RICE

SPRING LAMB, MINT SAUCE

ROAST TURKEY, CRANBERRY SAUCE

GREEN PEAS PUREE TURNIPS

BOILED RICE

BOILED & ROAST POTATOES

PLUM PUDDING

WINE JELLY COCOANUT SANDWICH

AMERICAN ICE CREAM

NUTS ASSORTED

FRESH FRUIT

CHEESE BISCUITS

COFFEE

Dinner menu from the Titanic.

Chapter Eight
Titanic - Day five

Sunday, 14 April started much the same as the previous few days for Elizabeth and her daughter, although Elizabeth was first out of bed on this morning and was looking out of the porthole when Edith stirred. 'Sorry if I woke you, dear,' said her mother, turning away from the porthole and looking towards Edith on the top bunk. She then went on, 'It's so calm out there again this morning, I just can't believe that we could have such good weather on this trip'. A short time later, Thomas tapped their door as usual, to let them know he was up and about and would be waiting for them to join him up on deck. They enjoyed their regular walks around the boat deck in the mornings before breakfast, allowing the sea air to give them an appetite before going down to the dining saloon. Once up on deck, they soon realised that, despite being a nice day, it was much colder than they had realised and certainly the coldest day so far this voyage. After a quick brisk walk around the boat deck, they decided that they should go below before getting any colder.

In the dining saloon, several other passengers commented on the drop in temperature and also the increased vibration felt in their cabins during the night. On the bridge at 9 a.m. an ice report was received from the Cunard Line vessel, the Caronia, reporting an icefield, 42 degrees north to longitude, 50 degrees west. This gave a position ahead of the Titanic, but to starboard, and not on her track. At noon, the Titanic's position was worked out and the distance logged since noon the previous day. It was 545 nautical miles giving her a speed of almost 23 knots. The air temperature at that time was 48 degrees and steady.

At 11 a.m. a Church of England service was held in the second class dining saloon, conducted by the Assistant Purser, the third class also being invited to attend, if they wished. In one of the first class public rooms, a service was also held at this time, conducted by Captain Smith. After the Sunday services, passengers chose to stay below decks to keep out of the cold, the ship creating a considerable wind chill up on the open decks. At 1.40 p.m. White Star Line's east bound liner, the Baltic reported ice in a similar position to that, reported earlier by the Caronia. Five minutes later, at 1.45 p.m. the ship, Amerika reported ice again, in the same position as that indicated by the previous ice reports. These ice reports suggested quite clearly that a huge icefield was slowly drifting south with the current.

At 5.45 p.m. Captain Smith was on the bridge for the expected course alteration which would take them some 16 miles further south than their intended course. Studying the chart and those ice reports that had reached the bridge, he reckoned that this course adjustment should steer them well clear of the icefield. At this time the air temperature had dropped three degrees and the sea temperature was down to 33 degrees. Before dinner that evening, the Browns decided to brave the cold and went up on deck to witness an almost glass-like calm sea and a beautiful sunset. Once again it was too cold to remain up there for long and, after taking in the splendour of the setting sun, they went below to take their seats in the dining saloon. During the meal, the conversation came round to the possible presence of icebergs in the area and the noticeable drop in the temperature during the day. Edith, taking it all in, said to Thomas, 'Do you think we'll see any icebergs, father?'. Her father replied, 'If there are any about, my dear, I doubt if we'll see any during darkness'. And then added, 'We'll keep a sharp eye open tomorrow and see if we can spot one'. Mrs. Carter joined in saying, 'I hope we see one before this trip is over. I've never seen one before'.

At 7.30 p.m. the freighter, Californian spotted a huge icefield in a similar position as those other reports received during the day. After dinner that evening, the Browns attended their second Sunday service in the second class lounge, this time conducted by the Reverend Carter. Of the several hymns chosen for the service, the final one to be sung, ironically, was, 'For those in peril on the sea'. At 9 p.m. the air temperature had fallen to just one degree above freezing. Travelling at 23 knots, the lookouts up in the crow's nest would have known all about it. They had scant protection up there against the elements, their only protection being a canvass 'dodger' about chest high and there was virtually no room to move about in, with two of them up there. It was at this time that the officer of the watch had informed the ship's carpenter to check on the ship's fresh water supply for any sign of freezing. At 9.45 p.m., another ice report came in from the ship Messaba again giving the same position of a massive icefield that lay ahead. At 10 p.m. that evening, Elizabeth and Edith decided to retire to their cabin for the night, leaving Thomas to return to the smoking room after escorting

Lifeboat 14 Passenger List

FIRST CLASS PASSENGERS

Mrs Mary Eliza Compton
Miss Sara Rebecca Compton
Miss Daisy Minahan
Mrs Lillian Minahan

SECOND CLASS PASSENGERS

Mrs Elizabeth Catherine Brown
Miss Edith Eileen Brown
Miss Clare Annie Cameron
Mrs Ada Maria Clarke
Mrs Charlotte Collyer
Miss Marjorie Collyer
Mrs Selena Rogers Cook
Mrs Agnes Mary Davis
Master John Morgan Davis
Mrs Esther Hart
Miss Eva Miriam Hart
Mrs Amelia Lamore
Mrs Juliette Marie-Louise Laroche
Miss Louise Laroche
Miss Simonne Anne-Marie Laroche
Mrs Alice Adelaide Louch
Mrs Elizabeth Mellinger
Miss Madeline Mellinger
Miss Nellie Walcroft
Mrs Adelaide Wells
Master Ralph Lester Wells
Miss Joan Wells
Mr Charles Eugene Williams

THIRD CLASS PASSENGERS

Mrs Bella Moor
Master Meier Moor
Mr. Edward Ryan
Mrs Thelma Thomas

CREW

Fifth Officer Harold Godfrey Lowe (in charge)
A.B. Seaman Joseph Scarrott
Window Cleaner William Harder
Leading Fireman Thomas Threlfall
Fireman Frederick Harris
Saloon Steward George Frederick Crowe
Bath Steward Frank Herbert Morris
Steward Alfred Pugh

RESCUED FROM THE WATER

Mr Patrick Doyle, third class passenger
Mr William Fisher Hoyt (died), first class passenger
Mr Fang Lang, third class passenger
Mr Harold C. Phillimore, Saloon Steward
Mr Emilio Portaluppi (possibly), second class passenger

them to their cabin.

At 10 p.m. the two lookouts going on watch were told by the officer of the watch to keep a sharp lookout for ice. They would first bang the bottom of the ladder with a shackle, to warn those in the nest that their reliefs had arrived, and to let one come down first. Once down, a relief would climb up the small iron ladder inside of the hollow mast, to allow the other to get down and so on. At 10.30 p.m. the sea temperature had dropped to 31 degrees. The British cargo ship, Rappahannock had signalled by Morse lamp to the Titanic to say that she had just passed through a huge icefield. This was acknowledged by the officer of the watch and, after entering it in the ship's log, continued to maintain the same course.

In the public rooms, passengers were enjoying their evening playing cards, or chatting among themselves over a drink or two, as the ship's orchestra played popular tunes of that time. At 11 p.m. the freighter, Californian attempted to transmit to the Titanic warnings of heavy ice, but was cut off by the Titanic's wireless operator due to his heavy workload sending out passengers' messages. After an hour in the crow's nest, Fred Fleet and Reginald Lee were beginning to feel the bitter cold and couldn't wait for their relief at midnight. At 11.30 p.m. both men noticed a slight haze up ahead and commented on it to each other. Just before 11.40 p.m. both men stared intently ahead. There was without doubt a huge haze looming up ahead, taking on more of a fixed shape as they got even closer. Five seconds, maybe more, passed before it finally revealed itself. It was a massive iceberg dead ahead.

Fleet grabbed the phone while Lee rang the bell three times as hard as he could. The high-pitched whine from the phone in the wheelhouse made the junior officer jump, before he rushed over to pick up the hand set. 'What do you see?', asked the officer. 'Iceberg dead ahead!', shouted Fleet. The junior officer turned to First Officer Murdoch and repeated what he had just heard, 'Iceberg dead ahead, sir!'. Murdoch, straining his eyes to see out of the windows, shouted, 'Hard to port!'. And then he issued the command, 'Full astern, all engines!'. He then rushed out on to the starboard wing of the bridge. In the crow's nest, Fleet and Lee, watched in utter amazement as a huge iceberg loomed up out of the darkness, getting bigger with every second. The Titanic steering straight for it, appeared to approach the iceberg at ever greater speed. Slowly, so slowly, the Titanic began to turn to port. As the lookouts in the crow's nest and the officers on the bridge watched with growing horror, it was becoming all too clear that she just wasn't going to make it.

Chapter Nine

Titanic - Day six

It was 1.30 a.m. Monday, 15 April. Most of the women and children destined for lifeboat no. 14 were already in the boat. Elizabeth and Edith were ushered along by a crewmember saying, 'Come on, ladies! Quick as you can!'. Elizabeth, turning her head around, shouted at Thomas, 'Get into another boat, Tom!'. She implored him to go round to the other side to try to find a boat. Elizabeth, almost falling as she was helped into the boat, started to cry again. Edith sitting alongside her mother, with tears in her eyes, looked back towards her father. He was making no attempt to find another boat and just stood there, puffing his cigar, never taking his eyes off them.

Suddenly another rocket streaked into the night sky with a loud hiss as it shot skyward, shooting out sparks as it arced over at the top of its climb, lighting up the faces of those people who briefly looked up. 'Stand by to lower away!' shouted Officer Lowe. At that precise moment, several men surged forward in an attempt to get into the hanging lifeboat. Bang! Bang! Bang! Three shots rang out in quick succession from Officer Lowe's pistol. He had aimed it away from the men and was using the shots as a warning. Women in the boat started to scream and children started to cry. Officer Lowe shouted to the men on deck, 'Try that again and it will be you I shall be aiming for!'. He pointed his gun in their direction and told them to get back away from the boat. They slowly retreated from the officer with the pistol.

'Lower away together!', shouted Lowe again to the crew on deck. Slowly, and in jerky movements, the boat started to descend to the black icy waters below. Officer Lowe thought about the weight in his boat and how the boat davits would stand up to the jerking descent, but realised there was little he could do about that now. Life-saving equipment on this ship was more of an after thought, he was beginning to realise, and the sooner they got down to the water the better he would feel. Edith looked up as another distress rocket lit up the sky and once again her mother shouted up to her father in panic, 'Find a boat, Tom! Get into a boat on the other side, Tom!'. Thomas remained standing in the same place on the deck and was now joined by the Reverend Carter, as he continued to wave to them as the boat went lower. Edith looking back up at her father, cried out in desperation, 'Do what mother says. Find a boat father!'. Tears were streaming down her face. Thomas blew them both a kiss, knowing the situation was hopeless for the men left behind. There wasn't enough room for all of the women and children in the boats, let alone the men. The boat continued its jerky descent down the ship's side and just before Thomas disappeared out of sight, he stepped forward, cupping his hands around his mouth and shouted down to them, 'I'll see you in New York!'. These were the last words they would ever hear from him.

Fifth Officer Lowe sat in the stern of the lifeboat, praying that the ropes and tackles would hold out until they reached the water. As the boat continued to be lowered, Edith noticed through the lighted portholes that some people were still below decks, grabbing what they could out of their cabins. Just before reaching the water, one end of the boat stopped while the other end continued down. Officer Lowe immediately could see what the problem was and shouted as hard as he could to the men up on deck to stop lowering. The rope had jammed in the tackle and it would take a tremendous effort to free it with this load on board. He shouted again to those on deck but it was futile, they just couldn't hear from all the din going on around. As one end kept going down there was a real fear that everyone would be tipped out of the boat. There was only one option. Lowe shouted at the able seaman at the high end, 'Get your knife out and cut the bloody ropes!'.

Passengers were beginning to scream and fall over each other as the seaman began to saw through the ropes with his knife. Suddenly, it gave way, and there was a great splash as the high end of the boat fell the last metre or so and splashed into the sea. Passengers now fell the other way, screaming and shouting with some completely upturned, with their feet in the air. Elizabeth quickly pulled Edith up from where she had fallen into the bottom of the boat, when there was another shout. 'There's water shooting up from a hole in the bottom!' The force of the impact on the water had forced the plug out of the bottom of the boat. 'The bloody plug has come out!', shouted the seaman to Officer Lowe. 'Get it back in as quick as you can!', shouted Lowe. Ship's lifeboats have plugs to enable rainwater to be drained when stowed on board. The plugs are chained adjacent to the hole and are usually easy to get at. However, with a boat full of people falling over each other, it was a different matter. The seaman, after getting people to move out of the way, managed to plunge his hand into the icy water and locate the plug, but only after almost six inches of water had found its way into the bottom of the boat. This left them all now sitting in the boat with water slopping around their feet. Edith looked down at her feet and noticed her favourite button-up boots were soaking wet with seawater, these lovely boots that her father had bought her in London.

Once the boat had settled in the water, the hooks were released at each end and the boat pushed away from the ship's side with oars. Looking through the portholes at sea level, they could see water lapping around the furnishings in the cabins. This once beautiful ship was now slowly dying. As they began to pull away, Edith noticed the portholes towards the forward section of the ship were now submerged and the lights were still shining under the water. Fifth Officer Lowe made towards another three lifeboats grouped together and took overall charge, organising an even distribution of passengers between all boats. All four boats, now tethered together, bow to stern in a single line, began to pull together away from the stricken liner to get a safe distance from the ship. Sitting hunched over in the lifeboat, Elizabeth raised her head to look back at the ship and to fix her gaze on the place on boat deck where she last saw Thomas. Edith, as though reading her thoughts, said to her mother, 'I expect he's gone round to the other side to try and get into a boat there, mother'. Elizabeth had stopped crying by this time and replied to her daughter by saying, 'Oh God I hope so!'. She despairingly commented that he didn't even have a life jacket on. Again she lowered her head and started to weep. Edith put her arms around her mother in an attempt to comfort her, tears falling easily down her own cheeks.

Another distress rocket streaked up from the Titanic's bridge, arcing over and lighting up the immediate vicinity with its star burst. As soon as Officer Lowe decided they were far enough away to avoid being sucked under when the ship finally sank, he ordered his boat's crew to 'rest oars'. They stopped rowing, leaning on their oars, and silently looked back at the Titanic, her bows now almost submerged. Around the lifeboats it was quiet, save for a sob now and then or a cough, as most of them looked towards the stricken liner, hardly believing what they were witnessing. From across the still water, came increasing shouts and screams along with bangs and crashing noises and the grating and creaking sounds of tortured metal. From the boats, there was a whimper now and then, a child starting to cry again, puffs of steam coming from people's mouths and nostrils, as the water gently lapped around the planking of the lifeboats. The Titanic's stern was now high out of the water, her three huge bronze propellers dripping water, visible because of the ship's lights reflecting on the water. Masses of people were making their way to that end of the vessel to flee the ever-approaching water creeping along the ship's decks. Music could still be heard coming from the boat deck, intermingled with all the other noises of the ship dying, the whole scene becoming eerie and extraordinary.

At this time, all the third class passengers from the forward section of the ship were now at the rising stern end. There were gates situated below decks, separating third class from second class and these had been kept closed throughout the ordeal. Many of the men that had arrived from the forward end were now assembled on the after well deck and the poop deck but there was no access to the boat deck from here. As a result, some of the fitter men were seen to be climbing along the jibs of cranes and also up the deck housing to get to the boats. Below decks there were angry scenes as groups of people were banging and rattling the closed metal gates, demanding they be opened. The stewards told them that they would be opened once the order was given. One emigrant shouted through the gate at a steward, 'If I get my hands around your bloody throat I'll throttle ya!'. There were cries for the gates to be opened for the sake of the women and children. Another surge by several burly men saw the gates give way. As they crashed down on the deck, some people were trampled on including Kate O'Mara's father who had his ankle trapped in a metal grille. After being freed by another man and then supported by his daughter, they made their way across the sloping deck and sat down, leaning against a ventilator. Holding his ankle and in extreme pain, he noticed the look of anxiety on his daughter's face. He insisted that she go up on deck and find a boat.

At that moment, Patrick Doyle arrived on the scene and said jokingly, 'This is no time to be taking a rest, you know?'. 'Rest be damned!', exploded Kate's father clutching his ankle. Patrick noticed the pained expression on his face and, nodding towards his ankle, asked what the matter was. Looking up at Patrick, he replied that he thought his ankle was broken. He cried to Patrick to get his daughter on a boat. He said there was no time to be lost. Kate cried out, 'You cant stay here Dad!'. 'I bloody well can!', exclaimed her father and he added, 'Go with him and find a boat before they're all gone!'. He continued with pain in his voice, 'You've got your whole life ahead of you. Now go!'.

Patrick grabbed her firmly by the hand and pulled her behind him. He promised her that he would go back for her father once he had put her safely into a boat. They ran through the second class accommodation, up several flights of stairs, took a number of wrong turnings, bumping into people as they went. Finally, they arrived up on the boat deck, to find most of the boats had gone, save for one that was in the process of being lowered. Patrick shouted out, 'Hold on! I've got one more for ya!'.

As the lifeboats circled the stricken liner at a safe distance, the occupants could see that the forward section had now completely disappeared below the surface of the water. The stern of the vessel rose forever higher out of the sea as hundreds of people were seen to be clambering towards that end to get away from the approaching icy water. There were thunderous noises coming from deep within the hull, followed by shouts and screams echoing across the still water. Edith and her mother watched and listened in horror to all that was happening about them, finally, putting their hands over their ears to block out the sounds of human suffering. Suddenly, there was a shout from one of the crew, 'The funnel is falling over'. With that there was a gasp from the boats as the forward most funnel, appeared to teeter over, before finally crashing into the sea amid clouds of steam and a shower of sparks, accompanied by more shouts and screams. People were seen jumping from the ship's stern as it rose ever higher, and then suddenly, instant darkness, as all the

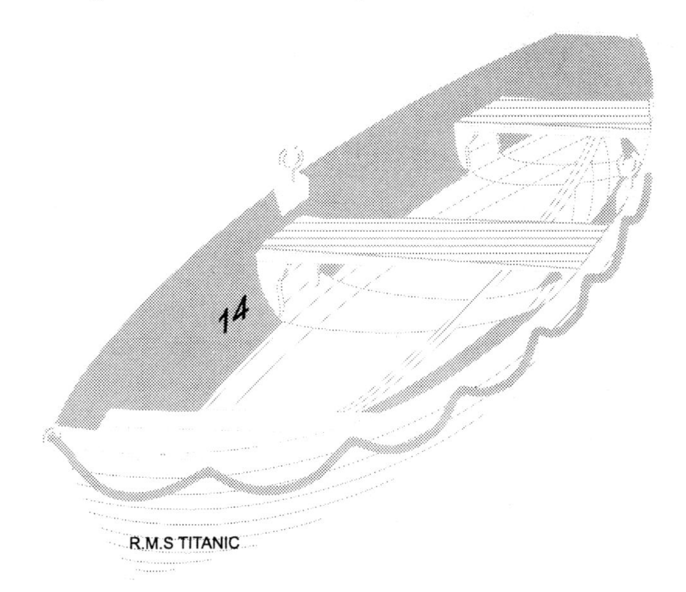

ship's lights failed.

Crashing and booming noises, along with heavy thuds, could be heard from within the Titanic, as huge parts of heavy machinery broke away from their fastings, and rumbled through the ship towards the submerged forward sections. With her stern now almost vertical, pointing up towards the starlit sky, there was an ear-shattering screech of metal being wrenched apart by great forces, as the once mighty liner broke her back. Her stern settled back momentarily, the screams and shouts for help unbearable as people in the lifeboats whimpered and sobbed, watching this horror of horrors unfolding before them. After several minutes, her stern rose up again, her massive bronze propellers coming out of the water once more and then spiralling, the whole stern section began to descend to the depths, following the now disappeared forward section into the sea. The screams and cries for help were drowned out briefly as sounds like huge underwater explosions erupted, sending huge volumes of spume to the surface as the Titanic's flagstaff at the very stern, finally disappeared below the sea.

The gurgling and bubbling noises began to abate as the surface of the water began to settle, leaving behind a slight mist as hundreds of cries for help could be heard once again. 'Make way together!', shouted Officer Lowe as they began to pull on the oars, heading back to where the Titanic had once been. The cries for help were scattered over a wide area and one man shouted from one of the other boats, 'They'll flood the boats and take us all down with them!'. Fifth Officer Lowe shouted back, 'Shut up! They'll all be too bloody cold to take anyone down with them!'. He gave the order to stand by to pick up survivors. Edith was sitting cuddled up to her mother, her favourite button-up boots splashing in the water in the bottom of the boat, her feet no longer having any feeling in them. Although the baling out of the water in the boat had taken some time it didn't appear to have made much difference to the water level in the bottom. As the 45 occupants in lifeboat no. 14 sat huddled together, the last thing on their minds was the water lapping around their feet after what they had all just witnessed.

That night, the lifeboats drifted around the wreck site in an area almost four miles in circumference, everyone suffering the effects of the extreme cold. The large lifeboats hanging from davits on the boat deck had a capacity, when full, of 65 persons each but on leaving the Titanic many of them fell well short of that number.

LIFE BOATS

Accident boats 1 and 2 had a capacity of 40 persons and the four collapsible boats, 47 persons each. The tally for each of boats was as follows:

Lifeboat no. 1 had only 12 people on board despite having a capacity of 40 persons.
Lifeboat no. 2 had only 25 people on board despite having a capacity of 40 persons.
Lifeboat no. 3 had an almost full complement of 65 persons.
Lifeboat no 4 had about 50 persons despite having a capacity of 65 persons.
Lifeboat no. 5 contained mostly women and children, only 45 persons despite having a capacity of 65 persons
Lifeboat no. 6 was almost full with mostly women and children on board.
Lifeboat no. 7 was almost full with mostly women and children on board.
Lifeboat no. 8 had 28 persons, mostly women and children on board.
Lifeboat no. 9 was overcrowded and distributed some to other boats.
Lifeboat no 10 took on more to even up distribution.
Lifeboat no 11 was overcrowded with more than 70 on board and off loaded some to other boats.
Lifeboat no. 12 had 40 women and children on board and picked up a further 30 from around the sinking ship.
Lifeboat no. 13 took survivors from other boats to even up the load.
Lifeboat no. 14 was Edith's boat with 45 on board. They picked up another four from the water, one died.
Lifeboat no. 15 was filled with mostly women and children, short of full capacity.
Lifeboat no. 16 had 56 persons on board.
Lifeboat collapsible A had 12 persons on board with a capacity of 47 persons
Lifeboat collapsible B overturned with 24 men balancing on upturned hull.
Lifeboat collapsible C had 39 women and children.
Lifeboat collapsible D was taken into tow by lifeboat no. 14 and passengers more evenly distributed.

Copy of newspaper article published in a Capetown paper reporting the death of T.W.S. Brown who was drowned in the sinking of the RMS Titanic on 15 April 1912. (newspaper date about 23 April 1912)

The Titanic Disaster
Drowning of Mr T.W.S. Brown (formerly of the Masonic Hotel)

'We learn from Mr J.H.P. Bosman, Napier St, Worcester, that he had received an intimation from his son, Mr W. Bosman, Capetown, that he had on Tuesday had had a cable from America announcing that his wife?s father, Mr T.W.S. Brown was one of the passengers who went down in the ill-fated Titanic and was drowned. Mr Brown?s wife and youngest daughter, who were accompanying him were saved in the boats.
We gather from further inquiries that the late MrBrown sailed from Capetown fully two months ago with his wife and daughter, and had resided in London for a time pending the sailing of the Titanic, as they had made up their minds to cross over to America in the magnificent new ship, with disastrous results.
Mr John W. Bosman (mayor) has favoured us with other interesting particulars of the deceased gentleman with whom he had been in touch, more or less, since his departure from Worcester some ten years ago.
Mr Thomas William Solomon Brown had been associated with hotels in South Africa prior to acquiring the Masonic Hotel, Worcester, in the ownership of which he remained for about eight years. He raised and well maintained the reputation of the hotel, and during the war (Boer) made it a lucrative business. He made a good name also for himself, as a reliable man whose word was his bond, and whose character was above reproach. He never sought public position or notoriety, but with his wife and daughters devoted his whole attention to his private affairs. Eventually he disposed of his hotel to Mr J.Carrol for twelve thousand pounds and retired with his family to the suburbs of Capetown. His investments were mostly in cottage property in Muisenberg, Kalk Bay and other places and he was more or less interested in hotels in Johannesberg and Bloemfontein.
Mr Brown?s first wife had predeceased him, and he had married again before coming to Worcester. The first family comprised two sons and two daughters, one of the latter marrying Mr W. Bosman of Capetown whilst they were resident in Worcester.
Mr Brown had only one daughter by his second wife, both of whom were accompanying him to the United States at the time of his death. Just before his departure from Capetown, Mr J.W. Bosman met him in Adderley Street, and, speaking of his intention to proceed with his wife and daughter to join relatives in America said he had disposed of all his property about South Africa and only retained some shares in the western Wine and Brandy Co. to remind him of Worcester and the people he had known there. He always entertained warm feelings towards them.
Mr Brown was over 60 years of age. Nothing is known of the intentions of Mrs Brown and daughter rescued from the Titanic, nor whether they were able to save any of their effects. The probability is that everything they were taking to America went down with the ship. News now anxiously awaited by mail.

As the early hours of the morning approached, there was silence across the water apart from a cough now and then, someone crying, and the water gently lapping the sides of the boats. The cold had its searching effects on all of them as they waited for daybreak and, hopefully, rescue. Several hours later as dawn broke, the scene before them was one of enormous and unbelievable tragedy. There were bodies everywhere, many of them with life jackets on, floating silently in an upright position. Among the corpses were many women and children frozen to death, still clutching hold of each other as they drifted among the ice floes. As daylight approached, it could be seen that they were in the middle of a vast icefield with several small icebergs scattered around in a vast area. During the night, one of the four picked up by lifeboat no. 14 had been found floating on some wooden gratings and, being soaked to the skin, couldn't have lasted much longer. It was to be Patrick Doyle's lucky day, although sitting in the boat wrapped in a blanket, he still looked in a bad way. Floating with the ice, there appeared to be a stoker, only in his vest, frozen to death, still clinging to some deck chairs tied together.

As they slowly made their way through the icefield, Officer Lowe ordered a sail to be hoisted, not so much to help them along because there was little breeze, but more to increase their chances of being spotted when rescuers arrives. Edith, trying to blot out the horror of this night, began thinking of the beautiful gold and coral necklace her father had bought her in London. She remembered leaving it on her bunk when going to the lifeboats, but now, it would be at the bottom of the ocean. On that same day in London, she also remembered her father buying her mother a beautiful gold and ruby dress ring encircled with diamonds. She quickly looked down at her mother's hands folded in her lap, and thank God, she was still wearing it. Elizabeth, as though reading her daughter's thoughts, spoke for the first time, after what must have been, several hours of silence throughout the night. She said softly, 'All we can hope for now is that your father has been rescued'. She went on in almost a whisper, 'Nothing else matters any more'.

At around 6 a.m. there was a shout from one of the boat's crew, bringing many of the occupants back to life. 'I can see a steamer's lights!', he shouted. Officer Lowe shouted back, 'Where do you see it?'. Pointing up ahead of them, the seaman shouted again, 'You can just see her masthead light! 'Officer Lowe, now standing up on the seat in the stern of the boat, exclaimed, 'By Christ you're right! It's the Carpathia'. To many of them in the boat, the Carpathia appeared to be hardly moving at all, but they could not realise that the ship was in the same icefield that had sunk the Titanic. Captain Rostron of the Carpathia had a huge responsibility on his hands, with every minute vital, in attempting to rescue the survivors from the extreme cold. He also had 700 passengers of his own to consider as well as his crew and his ship. He was now entering a deadly icefield.

The Carpathia slowly picked her way through the ice, stretching the patience of one member of the crew who shouted out, to no one in particular, 'For Christ's sake, get a bloody move on! We'll all be dead before you get here!'. Unknown to them at that time, the ship had already picked up some survivors, and was approaching them far more quickly than they realised. It was just that their anxiety was affecting their mental state. A small rope ladder was hanging down from the open shell doors as they drew alongside, as crowds of Carpathia's passengers were seen to be leaning on the ship's rail to watch. Many of the survivors were helped on board by crewmen from the Carpathia, who jumped into the lifeboat to help them up the short ladder. For many, it was too much, their hands were unable to grip anything, so they were hoisted on board by bosun chair. They didn't have far to go, the Carpathia was only a quarter of the size of the Titanic making the lift up to the deck, a short one.

Elizabeth and Edith both had difficulty in standing and also found they couldn't hold onto anything with their hands, so they were also hoisted up on deck. Once on deck, they sat where they landed with stewardesses coming forward to help them off with their sodden boots. Edith's feet were completely blue and her mother was also in the same predicament. The stewardess rubbing Edith's feet and legs exclaimed, 'My God, young lady, we've got to get those feet of yours to turn pink again or we'll have problems'. Elizabeth, also receiving the same treatment, just sat there watching, expressionless.

Survivors continued to be lifted up by the bosun's chair, with some of the small children hoisted on board in mailbags and placed on deck that way. The stewards and stewardesses were there to receive each and every one of them and to lend what assistance they could. Without a doubt the crew had been well briefed on what to expect on their voyage to the wreck site and brandy, hot soup and bread rolls were dished out as soon as they arrived on board.

Edith and her mother were finally helped to their feet and, still very shaky on their legs, were helped into one of the lounges. Once seated, they were wrapped in blankets and given hot soup and rolls, with Elizabeth saying to her daughter, 'I don't think I've ever tasted anything so good'. With their circulation slowly returning to normal, Edith and her mother began talking to other survivors about the ordeal they had all endured over the past eight hours. The stories were similar with most of the women fearing for the safety of their menfolk. Their conversations were interrupted every time a boat came alongside with everyone rushing out to look over the side to see if there was anyone they knew. Elizabeth wanted to go out on deck to see for herself if Thomas was among the few men that were arriving, but was strongly advised to stay where she was as she had not yet fully recovered and was still too shaky on her feet. As they tackled their second mug of soup, Edith said to Elizabeth, 'There's got to be more to come, mother! Father said the ship was practically full when we left Southampton'. Her mother replied, 'I pray to God that your father is still out there in one of those boats'. Another shout went up, 'There's another boat coming alongside!'. With that survivors and Carpathia's passengers rushed to the ships rail to see who had arrived in the next boat.

Elizabeth finally managed to get to her feet and hobbled outside, Edith holding her arm as they looked over the side. It was the same story, mostly women and children along with the lifeboat's crew. Collapsible lifeboat C arrived alongside with 39 women and children, including Bruce Ismay, the White Star Line's managing director. Once on board, he went straight to the doctor's cabin, where he remained for the rest of the voyage, refusing to see anyone. As the last of the boats had come alongside it was beginning to look as though there were going to be many widows arriving in New York when the Carpathia docked. Among the survivors, were two American women who had wrapped their little dogs in shawls to resemble children. Once all the boats were empty, they were hoisted on board Carpathia by her derricks and stowed on deck for delivery to White Star's wharf in New York.

Elizabeth and her daughter, like so many other women on board were beginning to show signs of despair, as it was becoming clear that all lifeboats from the Titanic had now been accounted for. Of all the women that had been rescued that morning, only four were found to still have husbands. To offer a glimmer of hope, a rumour had begun that perhaps another ship had arrived in the area during the night and had picked up those still missing. These hopes were soon dashed when it was found that no other ships had even reported being in the area, let alone picking up survivors.

With the last lifeboat on board, Captain Rostron continued his search in the area, in the vain hope of still trying to find someone clinging to wreckage or debris, but it was beginning to look extremely hopeless. It was far too cold for anyone to last for long in those waters.

During the Carpathia's continuing search through the icefield, Captain Rostron had received a message from Bruce Ismay for transmission to the White Star offices in New York which read briefly, 'Titanic sunk. Great loss of life. Will contact you later. Ismay'. Several of those rescued were in the Carpathia's sick bay suffering mainly from hypothermia and frostbite. One of those in a serious condition, although stable, was Patrick Doyle. As the ship slowly steered a winding course through the icefield, the Reverend Anderson of the Carpathia held a service in the ship's library for those that had perished. Meanwhile, the crew of the Carpathia was busy reorganising their lives by giving up their cabins to the women and children who had been rescued. The passengers of the Carpathia, destined for a cruise to the Mediterranean, now found themselves helping out in a crisis and it brought out the best in them. They were mostly Americans and extremely generous, finding clothes to fit the survivors and giving up their own cabins to the women and children.

As time went by, it was becoming obvious to everyone that no more survivors would be found, and later, a count was taken by the Senior Purser and officers. The count revealed a tragedy of enormous proportions, a tragedy almost unbelievable in maritime history. Of the 2225 persons on board of the Titanic just twelve hours ago, there were now only 705 survivors accounted for. The only other ship in that area was the Californian, which had also been stopped all night in the icefield. She had now arrived on the scene alongside the Carpathia, far too late to be of any help, and offered to take some of the survivors off the Carpathia. Captain Rostron had refused, realising to put some people back in a lifeboat would be too traumatic for them. He suggested that the Californian remain in the area and continue to search for any survivors whilst he headed for New York. After agreement on this course of action with Captain Lord of the Californian, the Carpathia slowly altered course and began to navigate her way out of the icefield.

It took several hours of navigating through small icebergs, growlers and pack ice before speed could be increased, revealing the extent of the icefield in this area. Edith and her mother having been on deck for long periods in the hope of seeing another boat, began to feel cold and went into the lounge which now had mattresses and blankets spread all over the floor. They were both completely exhausted, and on entering the lounge, practically collapsed onto a sofa together, neither of them uttering a word.

Edith and her mother sat for some considerable time with their thoughts and, although both of them were very tired, neither of them slept. Finally, Elizabeth took her daughter's hand in hers and said softly to her, 'My dear, things are not looking good for your father'. She went on, close to tears, 'However, that doesn't mean that we should give up hope yet'. She continued, 'Although it's been said that there weren't any ships in the area, the chances are a ship may have picked up survivors without telling anyone and continued on to New York. It had been said by a crew member, to some of the women survivors, that some ships' radio communications were still not up to much and a ship may well have picked up survivors, and had trouble transmitting messages'. Elizabeth felt that this may be clutching at straws, but it was feasible, and it did give them something to hope for until they arrived in New York, when the whole outcome would then be revealed. Looking intently at her daughter, she went on, 'You do understand, don't you Edith?'. Her daughter lowered her head and burying her face into her mother's breast, began to cry. Elizabeth, stroking her daughter's hair, allowed the tears to flow freely down her own face.

Kate O'Mara had watched every boat that had been brought alongside since her own arrival, but like the rest, was beginning to fear the worst. There had been no sign of her father or that good-looking man that had taken her to the lifeboat, and now, not recognising anyone on board, she felt all alone. She remained curled up in one of the easy chairs in the lounge thinking about the night that had just passed. She had never been so cold before in her life and was finding it difficult to believe what had happened these past few hours. The crew had given her some blankets and pillows and an American lady had given her some decent clothes to wear. She wondered what might have happened to her father being left so helpless on deck and felt extremely guilty at leaving him there. She nestled further into the chair, pulled the blanket over her head and wept silently until finally, she fell sleep.

It seemed like hours had gone by when she was gently woken up by a steward, asking her if she would like to go into the dining saloon for the second sitting of lunch.

She sat up, rubbed her eyes and then, thanking the steward, rose out of the chair, realising for the first time just how hungry she was. As the Carpathia steamed towards New York, the weather deteriorated with an icy wind, rain and sleet, continuing throughout that first night. The accommodation was cramped with the ship having twice its normal passenger carrying capacity, but this was paradise to what most of them had just been through. All of those rescued knew that the crew and passengers of the Carpathia had done their level best, and no more could be asked from them.

On the second day on board the Carpathia, as she steamed towards New York, Kate O'Mara spoke with the ship's doctor who was doing his rounds. 'How are you feeling today?', he asked Kate. 'Oh, much better thank you sir', she replied in that beautiful soft Irish brogue of hers. She then went on, 'It's good to feel warm again after sitting in that freezing boat all night'. Looking at this beautiful woman before him, he replied, 'Yes, it always amazes me how quickly the younger ones pick up after an ordeal like that'. And then, changing his tone slightly, asked, 'Are you with anyone?'. 'Not now', she replied and then continued, 'I was travelling with my father in third class but . . .' the tears began to well up in her eyes as she went on 'I haven't seen him since'. As she wept quietly, the ship's doctor put an arm around her shoulders and said gently, 'Try not to upset yourself'. And then went on, 'We have some men down in the sick bay. Perhaps you may like to pay the hospital a visit and see if there's anyone down there you may recognise'. Kate wiping her eyes, replied softly, 'Thank you, sir. I shall do that'.

Patrick Doyle had been told earlier by the ship's doctor that it was his youth, good health and probably the alcohol he had consumed that night, that had kept him alive before he was plucked out of the sea. Apart from a couple of frost bitten toes, he was told he could get out of bed if he felt like it, but should not venture out of the sick bay until arrival in New York. As he lay there, lightly dozing, he had images of that black-haired beauty looking down at him. He felt he was having a beautiful dream. He heard her soft voice in the distance saying, 'Is he going to be all right?'. Then a man's voice almost from afar, saying, 'He'll be fine as long as he takes it easy for a while'. He snuggled further down into his hospital cot, feeling soft hands on his cheek and those same hands stroking the hair away from his eyes. This was a dream, it had to be, but something made him open his eyes. Looking down at him was that beautiful face, hair cascading down her cheeks.

'Mother of Jesus!', He exclaimed. 'I'm dreaming!' 'No, I don't think so', came that soft melodious voice. She then leaned back as he pushed himself up into a sitting position, saying, 'How did you get here?'. Searching his face, she replied, 'In the boat that you put me in, if you remember'. Letting his head fall back on his pillow, he exclaimed, 'Remember! I shall never forget it!' and then added, 'What a bloody night that was!'. She leaned over him again, concern on her face as she asked him, 'Did you not see my dad?'. Patrick pulled himself up into a sitting position again and studied the anxiety in her eyes. He knew there was no easy way to say this but he did his best by telling her gently what had happened. After he had put Kate in the boat, he went back there to help her father but he had gone. It was chaos with people falling about everywhere and sliding down the deck into the water. He finally added, almost in a whisper, 'Nobody stood a chance'. As she sat on the edge of his bed, he could see that she had started to cry. Reaching out for her, he drew her to his chest, stroking her hair as she sobbed quietly in his arms.

The day before they arrived in New York, Edith and her mother were feeling greatly improved after their experiences of the last few days. Like her mother had said, it would all come out once they had arrived in New York and perhaps her father may even be there waiting for them. This train of thought made Edith feel better and she was going to stick with it until she knew differently. Elizabeth knew it would take nothing short of a miracle to bring her dearest Tom back to her, and she also knew that she would have to prepare her daughter for the worst. Edith had idolised her father all her life, and he in turn had spoiled her since the death of her younger sister Dorothy.

Sitting in the lounge after lunch on their last day on board the Carpathia, Elizabeth said to her daughter, 'You know that practically everything we had to start up business in Seattle was in your father's Gladstone bag, don't you dear?'. Edith replied, 'I know that father had a great deal of money in that bag, mother'. Her mother went on, 'Well, that's at the bottom of the ocean now, and whatever the outcome in New York, the plans we had for Seattle just don't apply any more'. Edith looked at her mother and then down at her feet as her mother went on, 'We will have to continue on to Seattle anyway as there really isn't anyone else we know, other than your Aunt Josephine, and no doubt they will be expecting that'. She went on, 'Besides, the way things are looking, we're going to need all the help we can get'. Finally she said to Edith, 'What I'm trying to say my dear is that we don't have any money or visible means of support any more'.

Edith had never had to think about money throughout her life, but she knew what her mother was saying, although not really understanding the effect this would have on her future. The only thing that mattered to her at this time was if she would ever see her father again. After several minutes of giving their predicament some thought, she then said to her mother, 'If father has been rescued do you think he would want to stay in America after losing all that money?'. Sadly, her mother replied, 'I wouldn't think so my dear'.

Chapter Ten
New York

On a bleak Thursday night at 8 p.m. on 18 April 1912, the Carpathia slowly steamed up the Hudson River in New York, heading for the White Star berth. She was accompanied by a flotilla of small craft and tug boats, crammed with sightseers and photographers, many of them shouting through loud hailers to those on board the Carpathia. She stopped briefly at the wharf where the Titanic would have berthed, and unloaded all that was left of her, the lifeboats, with the name Titanic painted on the bow of each one.

The Carpathia then moved upstream several berths to the usual Cunard Line berth and, with the help of a tug, gently moored up alongside. For those passengers and survivors on the Carpathia the scene that greeted them on the dockside was overwhelming and it was a sight that Edith and her mother would never forget. It looked as though the whole of New York had braved the foul weather to come down to the wharves to witness the arrival of the Titanic survivors. As the gangways were placed into position there were shouts from the quayside up to the people leaning on the ship's rail, and a never-ending barrage of questions. 'Did you see many floating dead bodies?', someone shouted. Another shouted, 'Have you lost anyone?' and another, 'Do you need any money?' and so it went on.

Not surprisingly, the class system still applied and those going ashore before anyone else were the first class passengers, amid a blaze of flashbulbs and a surge of reporters waiting at the bottom of the gangway. They were soon protected by shore personnel and then whisked away in their own transport. The second class passengers were the next to come ashore with Elizabeth saying to Edith, 'Keep close to me and keep walking or you'll never get away from them'. Once on the dockside the pushing and shoving of the throng made it almost impossible for them to move, as several burly New York policemen made a way through for them. As they slowly made their way into the cargo shed, the police were shouting, 'Come on, you guys!' followed by, 'Make way for Christ's sake!' and then 'Get the hell outa here!'. Finally they shouted, 'Can't ya see these people have been through enough already!'.

Several port officials joined them, leading their group to some offices at the far end of the shed. It had been decided that all single women would be taken care of by the Women's Junior League of New York and would remain under their care until other suitable arrangements could be made. The generosity of the Americans during their stay in New York was something they would never forget. The third class finally disembarked, among those, Kate O'Mara and Patrick Doyle, hand in hand as they went down the gangway together. Like the rest they were besieged by reporters until finally, they were led away by Kate's uncle and his wife to a waiting cab. They were two people brought together by tragedy, two people out of thousands whose lives were to change forever, two people who were to find love out of such tragedy.

The full extent of the sinking of the Titanic was becoming clear, despite the many false reports from the world's news agencies. People became angry when they read that more children had died in the third class than men from the first class. Of the third class, 535 men, women and children were lost and only 175 were saved. In the second class, 165 men, women and children were lost and 200 were saved. In the first class, 128 women and children were lost and 200 were saved. Out of a crew of almost 900, only 215 were saved. Of the 23 stewardesses on board, three drowned giving up their places in the lifeboats for women and children. All seven of the ship's orchestra had drowned, playing music to the very end. Every mail sorter had perished trying to save sacks of letters and registered mail. All eight bellboys had perished, not being allowed into a boat because they were considered crew despite their ages. Every engineer had perished in his final attempt to keep the ship's utilities running. As a lasting tribute to those engineering officers, all engineers in the British Mercantile Marine, now wear a purple band between each gold band on their uniforms.

The headlines in most newspapers made grim reading as a total of 1520 souls had lost their lives in the freezing waters of the North Atlantic. On arrival at the hostel, Edith and her mother had a hot meal and bath, finally retiring for the night, quite exhausted by the day's events. The next day they were taken shopping and bought more clothes than they would ever need, the Americans going out of their way to make sure they would want for nothing. After a lengthy shopping spree, they were taken around several hospitals in New York to see if any survivors had been taken there, but all to no avail. They knew in their hearts that they would never see Thomas again and when they returned to the hostel, Elizabeth said to her daughter, 'It's just you and me now, Edith'.

After the Carpathia's arrival in New York, Senator William Alden Smith, lost no time in setting up an inquiry. The Americans knew that the British would also hold an inquiry as soon as all the crew returned to England. It was therefore considered essential that an inquiry be held before those crew members returned to England and because the events of that night would still be fresh in people's minds. As the Carpathia was steaming towards New York, White Star had chartered two vessels out of Halifax, Nova Scotia, to search the area for bodies. One of the vessels the Mackay Bennet had picked up over 300 bodies, putting those on ice that were identified and burying the remaining 112 at sea. Many of those that had been found wore heavy clothing and had life jackets on, but the sea temperature being two degrees below freezing had been the main cause of death. The other ship, the Minia continued searching for bodies for another week as the Mackay Bennet returned to Halifax with nearly 200 bodies on board. By the first week in May, the weather had deteriorated with strong winds and heavy rain, and fewer bodies were found. A few days later the search was called off. Some two weeks later another body was found by a passing steamer and was buried at sea.

The US inquiry got under way without delay and some of the able seamen were questioned at the start of the proceedings. The inquiry was held at the Waldorf Astoria Hotel and, shortly after the start of the proceedings, Bruce Ismay was called to give evidence. He was questioned closely about his role while on board of the Titanic and he had replied repeatedly that he was no more than just a passenger. He continued to say that the captain was always in full command of his ship, and Senator Alden Smith found it difficult to get him to deviate from that theme during the questioning. The lookouts were questioned about the instruction to look for ice. They replied that they had done just that. They were also questioned about the lack of binoculars, and had confirmed that they may well have seen the iceberg sooner, had a pair been available. They also maintained that there was no question of the iceberg being seen any sooner with the naked eye than it had been. It was also confirmed that the response from the bridge was instant once they had received the report from the crow's nest.

During their stay at the Women's Junior League in New York, Elizabeth sent a cable to her sister Josephine in Seattle. The message was to let them know that they were safe but Thomas was feared drowned. She hated to have to say that in the cable, her hand shaking the whole time as she wrote it down for the telegraphist, however, that's how it was and there just wasn't any other way to put it. She finished off by saying they would be taking a train interstate within a week. The newspapers were full of the Titanic disaster and Elizabeth and Edith scanned them each day in the hope that they may have found Thomas's body if nothing else. It was now beginning to look pointless to hope for any more news about any missing passengers from the Titanic so Elizabeth decided to make arrangements for their journey to Seattle.

Sitting in the lounge of the hostel one afternoon, Elizabeth explained everything to Edith about what she had finally worked out. Looking intently at her daughter, she asked Edith whether she remembered her saying that they had no money. Edith nodded so she went on to explain that was not exactly true. Edith looked at her mother somewhat puzzled as she went on, 'Whenever your father and I went on long journeys we always carried gold sovereigns sewn into our clothes in case things went wrong'. Robbery had always been a concern to Tom and Elizabeth so they hid the gold as a safeguard. Edith, now showing greater interest in what her mother was saying, studied her closer as she continued, 'I have 50 gold sovereigns hidden away and, after we have paid for our rail fare, I will ask your uncle who works in the National Bank in Seattle to exchange them for me'. Edith had never known her mother to confide in her in this way before and was beginning to realise that things were going to be very different from now on. She then asked, 'Haven't we got any money at all, mother?'. Her mother replied that they only had the gold but she wasn't sure what the shares were worth in the wine company back in South Africa.

Edith then asked her mother how she had managed to save 50 gold sovereigns from the ship when all they had was what they stood up in mother. Her mother, with a faint smile on her face, looked directly at her daughter and said, 'I'll let you in to a little secret. The coat I wore in the lifeboat had sovereigns sewn behind the collar, about 15 around the waist and something like 20 around the wide hem at the bottom'. She went on, 'It hung rather well don't you think?'. Both women looked at each other, smiling for the first time in over a week.

The US Senate Inquiry moved to Washington where other important witnesses appeared, including Captain Lord of the Californian. There was criticism regarding the failure of the Californian to investigate further the rockets sighted whilst they were stationary in the icefield that night of 15 April. The Californian's officers had tried a Morse lamp, had seen rockets and had decided after 2 a.m. that the ship had steamed away. The inquiry had concluded that the Californian had been in a position to come to the aid of the sinking Titanic and they should have made more of an effort to investigate further the rockets they sighted. The findings of the inquiry have been a matter of controversy to this very day. Senator Smith, in winding up his findings, accused those responsible for the safety of the Titanic as negligent and recommended sweeping changes for safety at sea.

During Elizabeth and Edith's stay in New York, they were hounded by the press everywhere they went. Elizabeth knew only too well that it was because of the press that so many people came forward to offer help and they would be forever grateful for that. They had been asked so many times what their future plans would now be and gave the same answer, that of going on to Seattle. It was as a result of this, that one morning on receiving regular mail from well wishers, they opened one particular envelope and found two train tickets inside for Seattle. On reading the enclosed card it brought tears to their eyes. It just simply said, 'Please find the enclosed tickets to happiness and a wonderful future'. It was anonymous. They were both overwhelmed by this act of kindness with Elizabeth saying, 'If only I knew who it was so that we could thank them'. Later that day when confronted by another reporter, Elizabeth asked him to print her and Edith's gratitude in his paper to the anonymous person or persons for those two train tickets, in exchange for an interview. He readily agreed.

It was decided that they would leave on the long interstate train journey to Seattle at the end of the week. They had no idea of just how far it was but they had been advised by many well wishers to prepare for a journey of anything up to five days duration. They did their final shopping around the stores, again people insisting on paying for everything and going out of their way to help in any way they could. Their last night in New York was one of sadness, feeling in a strange sort of way that they were finally laying Thomas to rest, a wonderful father and husband. There was also sadness at leaving so many kind people behind who had, in such a short time, become such wonderful friends. They would never be able to thank enough.

On arrival at New York's main station for their journey across America, Elizabeth and Edith were accompanied by several well wishers and the inevitable press. They were to journey through ten states totalling something like 2000 miles. They boarded their train with the help of a Negro porter who, when offered the customary tip, replied, 'No, ma'am. You's is Titanic folk and is gonna need every dime'. The huge locomotive with its great lantern situated on the front of its bell-shaped funnel and the 'cow catchers' at its front, began to slowly pull out of the station, with shouts of 'Good luck' from the well wishers left behind on the platform. Elizabeth, looking around their compartment with its Victorian-style drapes and tassels hanging about the windows said to Edith, 'I think we shall be comfortable here for the next few days, don't you think dear?'. Edith replying, 'Yes, It does look nice and cosy mother'.

As the train cleared the station and gathered speed, they settled back into their padded seats for the first leg of the journey to Cleveland, some 400 miles away. As they travelled through New York State, they went into the dining car for the evening meal and then later, to the sleeping car, both of them tired after another busy day. Throughout the night the train trundled through New York State and into Pennsylvania and by early morning, wonderful scenery came to life. Passing the Pocono Mountains and the breathtaking scenery through the Lake Erie region, known as a water-lover's paradise of lakes and rivers, they crossed into the state of Ohio. It was here in the early morning that they passed the township of Sandusky, with its historic houses and swimming beaches of Lake Erie.

On the morning of Tuesday, 2 May, they had arrived in Cleveland and, quite surprisingly, they were met by reporters again. Elizabeth, quite expert by now, told them what they wanted to hear and then dismissed them with relative ease. After an almost two-hour stop, they boarded the train again for the next leg of their journey, bound for Chicago. The next stage of this long train ride was along the banks of Lake Erie with river valleys and steep forested hills as they continued through the state of Indiana, bordering Lake Michigan. With summer fast approaching the scenery was quite spectacular at times. After arrival in Chicago, there was a change of trains and several hours wait until boarding for the next leg of their journey which would be to Minneapolis. This was a long haul of some ten hours, passing through the state of Illinois with its vast rich farmlands, reaching from Lake Michigan to the Mississippi River.

These long hours on the train were made bearable by looking out of the windows at the rolling plains and the hills and valleys of this beautiful state of Illinois. After the long journey from Chicago, Edith and her mother were relieved when the train finally pulled in to St Paul, known as the twin city to Minneapolis. Situated on the banks of the Mississippi, this fast growing town was known as a frontier town with its wide-open spaces and lakes. Again they changed trains and after a stop of just over an hour, continued on their journey through Minnesota, bordering Canada and Lake Superior, the largest freshwater lake in the world. Their train traversed through the many forests of the upper mid-west throughout the night, going into North Dakota, famous for its scenery and spectacular views. They stopped at Fargo, the biggest town in the state, before setting off again for Billings, on the eastern fringe of the Rocky Mountains. This was the state of General Custer fame, with its many canyons and rough riding country. On their arrival at Billings, they had time to get off the train and stretch their legs and to wash and brush up, before the next part of their journey, which would take them on to Spokane.

On Thursday afternoon, 4 May, they set off once again to their next destination, travelling through the state of Montana, known as one of America's most scenic states. This was a state of vast areas of wilderness, great ranches and cattle drives with much wildlife including, elk, deer and antelope. Edith and her mother were mesmerised by this wonderful scenery from their carriage windows, until darkness fell. They had their evening meal in the dining car before retiring for the night as the train wound its way through the spectacular Rocky Mountains. As Edith lay in her sleeper, her thoughts about Seattle no longer gave her any excitement. The loss of her dear father had changed everything and now it was just a matter of wait and see what develops when they get there. As she lay there with her thoughts, listening to the clatter of wheels beneath her, she slowly drifted into a deep sleep. During the night they had crossed over from the state of Idaho and entered into Washington State.

They were woken up by one of the restaurant staff calling out in singsong style, 'Spokane in 45 minutes! Spookane! Spooookane! We shall be arriving in Spokane in 45 minutes! The restaurant car is serving breakfast this very minute! Spoookane, Spokane! All those for Spokane!'. Edith and her mother felt like they had been on that train forever, but Spokane meant that the next stop would be Seattle. Once they had arrived in Spokane, Elizabeth sent a cable to Josephine to let her know their time of arrival in Seattle. After a stop of two hours, to take on water and refuel, they settled down again for their final leg of the journey, once again, taking in the wonderful scenery outside of their carriage window.

On arrival in Seattle, late on Friday afternoon, 5 May, they were once again confronted with reporters on the station. The Titanic had gone down almost three weeks ago and yet the newspapers were still full of it and it was still a good story. It was a chilly afternoon as the press threw question after question at them, preventing them from getting off the railway platform. They wanted to know how Thomas had drowned and asked lots of other insensitive questions that were beginning to take their toll on them. Before it went on much longer, Josephine and her husband George arrived on the scene and rescued them both, ushering them to their automobile. A porter followed behind with their luggage. Once away from the station, Elizabeth broke down and sobbed uncontrollably. Edith, seeing her mother once again so distressed, also broke down. Her aunt, sitting in the back with them, did her best to console them. The long train journey had been a distraction from their tragedy, allowing them to take in the wonderful refreshing scenery, so different to what they had been experiencing those past few weeks. To be confronted by all those reporters on their arrival at Seattle had brought it all back and it was just too much after such a long journey.

They drew up outside Josephine's house, which was situated in a leafy suburb of Seattle. George got out of the driver's seat and went back to open the door for the ladies, both Elizabeth and Edith now composed. As George organised their luggage, Josephine, on entering the house, turned and said to them both, 'First things first'. She went on, 'A hot bath and then something to eat and bed for both of you'. She continued, 'You have been through a dreadful time and both look thoroughly exhausted!'. Josephine had always been the bossy one in her family but on this occasion, Elizabeth was happy to let her take charge. She then went on, 'You can tell us all about it after you have rested and, in your own time, if you feel up to it'.

That evening, as they both took their hot scented baths, it was pure bliss and later, after their meal, they slept like never before. Edith and her mother slept for over 12 hours that night, to be woken the next morning by Josephine bringing them in a breakfast tray. She had also brought them the newspapers and one headline read, 'Titanic survivor reunited with sister in Seattle'. It then went on to mention how Edith, a 15-year-old girl, had been sitting in the lifeboat with her mother and that both of them had nearly frozen to death. It went on to describe those that had drowned and mentioned Thomas. Elizabeth, briefly flicking through the pages, chose not to read any more and also advised Edith to do the same. Josephine immediately realised that the newspaper had been upsetting and apologised to Elizabeth by saying, 'I'm sorry. I hadn't realised'. Elizabeth, cutting her off replied, 'Don't concern yourself over it, Jo, we've had this ever since the ship went down. We just can't be bothered to read the same thing over and over again'. Josephine went on, 'It must be hard for you both to try and avoid it. It's been in every newspaper now for weeks and with these inquiries going on, it's still making headlines'. With that, Josephine realised that they had both suffered enough and would never discuss the subject again unless they raised it first.

The Senate inquiry into the sinking of the Titanic was drawing to a close in Washington after most of the important witnesses had testified. One of those was Fifth Officer Lowe of lifeboat no. 14 who made a statement to confirm that the use of his pistol was only for warning men away from the boat. His priority was to get as many women and children into the boat as possible, and to prevent the danger of the boat becoming swamped with too many people. He maintained that there was no truth in the allegation that he had fired his pistol to prevent emigrants from getting into the boat, while other classes were given priority.

George, Josephine's husband, held a good position in the Seattle National Bank and was turning out to be a great help to Elizabeth and Edith. He had obtained the best rate available in exchanging Elizabeth's gold sovereigns and had also begun inquiries regarding Thomas's estate back in South Africa. As the weeks passed, it was becoming clear that there really wasn't any point in Elizabeth and Edith remaining in America now with Thomas gone. Josephine and her husband had done all they could to try and help them settle in, but there really wasn't any future for them in Seattle.

Elizabeth knew that George and Josephine were feeling some guilt for writing all those letters over the past year or so, telling them how America was booming and it was the place to start a new life. After dinner one evening, Josephine mentioned how she wished she had never tried to persuade them to sell up and come out there. Elizabeth would have none of it by saying to her, 'You must not blame yourselves for what was, an act of God, nothing else!'. Her South African accent quite strong, as she went on, 'How many other people were on that ship because they had friends and relations that had also persuaded them to go to America I wonder?'. She added, 'Are they to blame also?'. And then, 'Of course not! I beg of you both, not to burden yourselves with such thoughts'.

Later that evening as they were preparing for bed, Edith noticed the beautiful dress ruby ring her father had bought for her mother in London was now missing from her finger. Looking at her mother a little startled, she exclaimed, 'Your ring, mother! Where have you left it?'. Elizabeth, feeling guilty at not telling her before, looked at her daughter in a sorrowful way and told her that it had broken her heart to do so but that she had sold the ring in view of their situation. She said that she had no choice. She then went on to say that she had wanted to pay their way during their stay with Josephine even though they wouldn't have any of it. Elizabeth had insisted. The money from the gold sovereigns would not last them forever and there were hotel bills and sea voyages to England and then onto South Africa to consider. Elizabeth felt that if they were careful they should have enough. Edith nodded, looking down at the floor, realising that things had certainly changed over the past few weeks.

It was now the end of May and the time had come for Elizabeth and Edith to start preparing themselves for the long journey back across America. 'I'm definitely not looking forward to that long train ride again', Elizabeth said to Josephine on their last evening in Seattle. She went on to explain that she hadn't expected to spend such a long time on a train and would have taken more with her to pass away the time. She then went on to say that the scenery at times was too beautiful for words and that she wouldn't have missed that for anything. Josephine offered her some embroidery and crochet work. 'Oh, that will be wonderful!', replied Elizabeth and added, turning to Edith, 'You like crochet work, don't you dear?'. Edith said that she hadn't done any for years but would like to get back into it.

Josephine's husband, George, had been busy these past few days, organising their travel arrangements by rail and sea, with the help of his colleagues from the bank. It had been worked out that when they arrived in New York, they would be staying in a small downtown hotel for just two days before joining the White Star liner Celtic. The ship would sail for Liverpool on the 8 June and they would arrive in England around 15 June. They would then travel down to Southampton where a room had been booked for them at the Dolphin Hotel. They would stay there for just a week before joining the Union Castle liner Carisbrooke Castle, which was due to sail for Capetown on the 25 June.

On arrival at Seattle's railroad station, Elizabeth thanked George for all he had done for them these past few weeks. She said she didn't know what she would have done without his help. Turning her attention to Josephine, she said that she would always be indebted to her and would be in touch as soon as we arrive back in Capetown. George answered for both of them by saying that their hearts went out to both of them for the tragic way things have turned out. He then went on to say that he would never forget Thomas, but that life must go on now for their sake. He hugged them both and said finally, 'We wish things could have turned out differently but our only hope now is that you both find happiness again in South Africa'.

Elizabeth and Edith, with tears in their eyes, said their farewells and boarded the train. Once seated in their carriage, Elizabeth realised just how close she and her sister had become as the train pulled away from the station. Elizabeth and Edith arrived back in New York, some four and a half days after leaving Seattle. Although they had managed to pass away the time with their newfound needlework, they still felt very tired on arrival in New York. On leaving the train, Elizabeth said to Edith, 'Thank God that's over! I never want to see another train as long as I live!'. 'Me neither,' chimed in Edith.

After arriving at their hotel, they had a meal and a bath and being extremely travel weary, had an early night. The following morning, being Sunday, they attended church, just two blocks down from their hotel. After the service, Elizabeth said to her daughter, 'Your father is at rest now and when the time is right for us, we shall all meet again, of that I am certain'. Edith replied softly, 'Yes, I feel that too, mother'. Both women were extremely nervous at the thought of sailing on the Celtic the following day, but knew it was unavoidable. That night before retiring Edith asked her mother, 'Do you think there will be any icebergs this time, mother?'. Her mother, replying a little nervously, said, 'Oh God, I hope not!'. She then went on, 'The best thing for us to do is to shut everything out of our minds until we get to England'. Edith then said, 'Try not to worry mother. I don't think anything quite so dreadful could happen to us again'. Elizabeth began thinking how much more mature Edith had become over these past few weeks. She said that they should not dwell on it any more and try to enjoy the voyage if at all possible. With that they both got into bed, but neither of them slept at all well that night.

It was a beautiful summer's day, although humid, when they joined the Celtic at Pier 61 on the Hudson River in New York. They were to travel second class again, finding their two-berth cabin to be quite comfortable, although not up to the standard of the Titanic. Just before the bedroom steward left them to settle in, Edith, unable to get it out of her mind, asked him if there would be any icebergs on this voyage. His reply, 'Not at this time of the year, madam. It's only in the spring when the ice breaks away up in the north that it's a problem'. He then inquired, 'Someone has been telling you about Titanic, no doubt?'. 'No one has been telling us about the Titanic', Elizabeth answered for both of them, 'We were just unfortunate enough to have been on board at the time that's all'. 'Good grief!', exclaimed the steward, 'I had no idea. I do apologise most sincerely madam!'. He then went on, 'It must have been terrible for you. I trust I have not offended you ladies in any way.' Elizabeth, in a dismissive way, assured him that he had not. With that the bedroom steward made a hasty retreat, wishing them both a pleasant voyage on his way out.

The ship sailed at noon, both women relieved that icebergs would not be a threat this time crossing the North Atlantic. For the first two days out of New York, the weather was fine although there was dense fog at times with the ship slowing down and forever blowing its foghorn. Elizabeth elected to stay below most of the time, although Edith found the ship's library a good place to pass away the hours. She also ventured up on deck more so on her own than she would have done on the Titanic and began to talk more openly to other passengers. She would be 16 in October and, since the passing of her father, began to feel more adult, especially now that her mother was confiding in her more. During one of her short excursions on the upper decks, she got into conversation with an elderly couple who asked if she was the young girl who had been rescued from the Titanic. How they found that out so quickly she found it hard to understand, but remembered the bedroom steward who, no doubt, had passed it on to all and sundry. Back in their cabin, Edith said to her mother, 'It looks as though quite a few people know about us already'. Her mother replied, 'I'm not surprised'. She said that she knew what ships were like for spreading gossip around. She commented that it usually got better the longer it went on. Edith had to smile at her mother's matter of fact response.

So far during this voyage, Elizabeth had elected to remain below decks, just going to the dining saloon and then back to their cabin. Edith asked her why she preferred to just sit and read in the cabin all day instead of going up on deck. She replied, 'These past few days have been the worst for me knowing that we would be passing close to the area where your father must have drowned'. She went on, 'Just sitting in this cabin quietly by myself, I have on a number of occasions felt his presence and it's been a strange and wonderful experience'. She continued as though staring into space, 'I don't wish to frighten you my dear but I have this feeling that he is looking over us'. Edith replied, 'It doesn't bother me, mother, in fact, I think it's rather wonderful for you to feel like that'. She then continued, studying her mother's face, 'You must have loved father a great deal mother'. Elizabeth, turning to look at her daughter, replied, 'He was the most considerate, loving man anyone could ever meet and I feel somewhat honoured to have known him'. Edith, noticing the tears beginning to well up in her mother's eyes, finally said to her, 'That's a lovely thing to say mother. I feel like that too'.

On the Sunday before arriving in Liverpool, the usual church service was held in the ship's library and was conducted by the captain. During the service, Elizabeth and Edith were included in their prayers and also those souls that had perished on that tragic night of 15 April. The Celtic arrived in Liverpool on a fine clear morning and after disembarking, Elizabeth and Edith caught a train for Southampton. Elizabeth and her daughter were to stay at the Dolphin Hotel for just a week before joining their ship for South Africa. It was now summer in England and the walks through the Southampton parks and around the shops made them feel like their old selves again. During their stay there, Elizabeth wrote to Josephine, again thanking them for looking after them when in Seattle. She also wrote to Edith's eldest stepsister, a Mrs Bosman in Capetown, informing them of their arrival back in that country. During their stay in Southampton, Edith and her mother spoke at length about their future in Capetown and whether they would remain there or return to Rhodesia. It was all very uncertain and most of it depended on the kind of money that would be realised on Thomas's shares in the brandy and wine companies.

As they sat in the lounge of their hotel one afternoon having tea, Edith said to her mother, 'Do you remember when father was going up the gangway of the Titanic, how he became faint?'. Elizabeth slowly nodding her head replied, 'I shall never forget it, my dear'. She then went on, 'Your father told me afterwards that he had also had a similar experience when in Capetown when he first booked our voyages'. Elizabeth went on, 'He was also very unhappy about the incident, when leaving Southampton, of the Titanic nearly colliding with another vessel'. Edith looked quite puzzled and then said to her mother, 'Do you think father may have taken this as some kind of premonition?'. Elizabeth, again appearing to stare into space, replied to her daughter, 'Your father was a very religious man and had always maintained that we get signs in life that should be taken notice of'. She went on, 'He obviously thought that he should never have sailed on the Titanic'. Elizabeth began to choke back tears as she went on, 'This is why I feel so bad about it all. Don't you see my dear, despite his fears of travelling, he went through with it, just for us'. Edith could feel a lump in her throat as her mother, turning to her, said quickly, 'Don't upset yourself, my dear. Perhaps it's just me and there's nothing in it at all'.

They arrived at berth 46 in Southampton Docks on the 25 June and boarded the Carisbrooke Castle. It was a fine summer day as they strolled along the upper decks before sailing time. They stopped and looked across the dock basin at berth 43, now strangely empty. It was just nine weeks ago that the magnificent Titanic was lying here, bedecked in flags, in all her splendour. Now she was lying on the bottom of the North Atlantic, having taken over 1500 lives with her. Elizabeth, turned and looked at Edith saying, 'I still can't believe it! Your dear father! That beautiful ship! All gone, and us back here. It's just so unbelievable!'.

Chapter Eleven
Capetown

The Carisbrooke Castle sailed on time at 4 p.m. and the whole voyage there after was uneventful, apart from Elizabeth suffering bouts of seasickness in the Bay of Biscay. The weather settled down after that and both women began to enjoy the rest of the voyage, especially those wonderful tropical evenings as they approached the equator. On the morning of 13 July, they made the effort to get up early as the ship arrived at Capetown. At daybreak the Carisbrooke Castle slowly passed the breakwater on the way into her berth. It was a crystal clear morning as Elizabeth and Edith looked up at Table Mountain, standing out against the early morning sky with a slight mist lying about its base. Elizabeth, staring at the mountain, said softly to her daughter, without looking away, 'I never thought, on leaving here, that we would be back so soon'. And then turning to Edith said, 'We're home again my dear and that's all that matters'.

After disembarkation, they were met by Edith's stepsister and her husband on the dockside. They later went along Adderley Street, passing all the familiar places, including the Mountain View Hotel that was their home before going on this fateful journey. They then went on to Sea Point where they would be staying until the financial situation had been sorted out and alternative arrangements could be made. It was during their stay at Sea Point that Edith met her other two stepbrothers and stepsister who had all arrived for their share of Thomas's estate. One of the stepbrother's main concern was that they didn't have his father's gold pocket watch that was promised to him. Elizabeth saw red, after all they had been through. She was shocked that, after suffering the loss of Thomas, this was the only concern shown by this young man. Elizabeth had no time for such claims and told him in no uncertain terms that if he felt so strongly about the watch, he should start looking at the bottom of the North Atlantic for it.

With the help of solicitors, an agreement had been reached that the whole of

Thomas's estate would be shared equally between the six of them, being the four stepchildren and Elizabeth and her daughter. This had surprisingly turned out to be a sizeable sum, and once settled, Elizabeth decided the time was right to move on. Edith had never really known her father's children from his first marriage and she had noticed they showed some resentment towards her mother. She knew that her mother had loved her father dearly and considering what she had just been through, she didn't deserve to be treated like that. Like her mother, she was glad to get away from them all, moving into a comfortable flat in Capetown where they were to stay for the next two years.

On 30 July 1912, the British inquiry into the sinking of the Titanic published its findings and generally negligence was cited as the main cause of the disaster. The Titanic's navigators were considered negligent for allowing the ship to proceed at a speed that was reckless after so many ice warnings had been received. Captain Lord of the Californian was negligent for failing to make any rescue attempt after sighting distress rockets (an argument that goes on to this very day). The company were negligent for employing seamen who were inexperienced in the manning of lifeboats and also negligent for allowing the vessel to sail without sufficient lifeboats for those on board.

The British Board of Trade was negligent to pass such a vessel to go to sea and was also negligent in its failure to update the correct requirements for ships of such great tonnage. The British inquiry, which had opened on 2 May, and was conducted by Lord Mersey, had by the time of its conclusion on 21 June, interviewed over 95 witnesses. The majority of those interviewed were crew, with the exception of Sir Cosmo Duff Gordon, who was travelling in first class with his wife and secretary. He was questioned closely as to why he had offered money to members of the crew in the lifeboat they were in. His reply was that the moment the ship had sunk, the crew would have been 'off wages' and the vessel had sunk with all their kit still on board. His response had been that he and his wife had felt sorry for them and had offered a promissory note of five pounds each, for them to replace their belongings. It was also noted by the inquiry that their lifeboat had only 12 persons on board and that they never made any attempt to return to pick up other survivors.

Perhaps one of the most important witnesses of the whole proceedings was that of Second Officer Lightoller who was asked no less than 1500 questions throughout the whole inquiry. Being questioned by Mr Scanlon, it was put to him that more crew should have been used in each boat. Lightoller's reply to that was that, if that had been the case, then less passengers would have found room in the boats. Mr Scanlon then replied to that saying the ship should have carried more lifeboats. Lightoller was asked about binoculars not being available in the crow's nest and his reply was that he could offer no explanation as to why there were none available. The question of speed was raised during the questioning and Lightoller reckoned it to be around 22 knots. When challenged about pushing the ship too hard, he had replied that it was not White Star policy to push any of their ships hard for up to a year after they entered service.

The questioning continued with Mr Scanlon accusing the ship's navigating officers of utter recklessness in view of the ice reports received and the continuing speed of the vessel. Lightoller had replied that if that was the case then all other ships on the North Atlantic trade could also be called reckless, as he put it. There was the inference from Mr Scanlon that Captain Smith was far too busy socialising instead of being in his rightful place, which was on the bridge. Lightoller had answered this by saying that there was no truth in such an accusation and maintained that the captain was always on the bridge for any important decisions or whenever adverse weather conditions prevailed. Stewardesses were also questioned at the hearing and they had related how they had helped the ladies and their children with life jackets and had assisted in getting the women and children into boats. One of the stewardesses had previously been on a ship called the Lake Champlain which had also collided with an iceberg and knew the emergency procedure for abandoning ship in such an event.

The White Star Lines manager, Mr Bruce Ismay, was cleared of all charges made against him, as was Sir Cosmo Duff Gordon for not attempting to rescue anyone. The crew received little mention, other than criticism, although three quarters of them had lost their lives. For those that had survived, the company had stopped their wages just after midnight when it was known that the ship was doomed and the company no longer required their services. It was a disgraceful way to treat the crew, and the way they have been depicted, and criticised by numerous books and films over the years, has also left much to be desired. It was also considered reasonable for the third class to be kept away from boats until other classes had been accommodated. Such was the class system at the turn of the century and, more surprisingly, those classes expected that kind of treatment.

As 1912 drew to a close, it was a year never to be forgotten by many, especially those 705 survivors from the Titanic disaster. They, and those closely related to them, would have their lives changed forever. The great engineering and shipbuilding achievement that was Titanic had disappeared below the Atlantic in just two hours after all those years of planning. There were many lessons to be learned and, as a result, shipping, worldwide is far safer. After the inquiry, the Titanic's sister ship, the Olympic was immediately fitted with extra lifeboats, as the Board of Trade changed its lifeboat requirement for this new breed of ocean going liner. Mother Nature had dealt a lethal blow to mankind but the iceberg had silently continued to drift south with the currents, eventually, becoming part of the sea.

Within months of settling into their apartments in Capetown, Elizabeth began to show signs of generally becoming run down, showing a lack of interest in most things. By January 1913, she decided to seek medical advice, realising that her lethargy was having an effect on her daughter, which just wasn't fair. After tests and a lengthy discussion with her doctor, his diagnosis pinpointed the events of the past year as being the main contributory factor for her condition. His recommendation was for her to have a proper holiday and perhaps, go on a cruise. Elizabeth sat dumbfounded at his suggestion of going on another sea voyage and said to him, 'Are you really serious doctor?'. She then went on, 'I think I've had enough of ships to last me a lifetime!'. He smiled then leaning across his desk, patted her on the back of her hand, and said, 'It is the analogy of the horse and rider Mrs Brown! When you fall off, you get right back on! It is one of the best ways I know of facing up to a traumatic experience such as the one you've been through'.

In contrast, Edith had coped quite well during the past year, and was now a source of strength for her mother, who in turn was beginning to show quite a bit of reliance on her daughter. When her mother told her about the doctor's recommendation, Edith also showed surprise, knowing how nervous her mother could be. Several days later, Edith was absolutely amazed to find that her mother had actually gone through with her doctor's advice and was in the process of booking a cruise for both of them. It was finally arranged that they set sail on the Orient Line's cruise ship, Orsova at the end of the month for a four-week round trip to Australia.

It was summer in the Southern Hemisphere and the voyage across the Indian Ocean was pleasant all the way. Edith was quite surprised at the way her mother was settling down on this voyage and appeared to be enjoying herself. 'Just what the doctor ordered', said Elizabeth to her daughter one afternoon as she stretched back, relaxing in a deck chair, the steward serving them ice cold drinks. Elizabeth had chosen first class for this trip as money was no longer a problem, their share of Thomas's estate being quite substantial. After dividing up his estate six ways, the sum of money for each individual left Elizabeth with the realisation that her late husband had indeed been a wealthy man. The Orsova was a comfortable ship, carrying some 700 third class emigrants to Australia and the second class full with 130 passengers.

Their first port of call was Sydney and, on going ashore, Edith and her mother had a good day tripping around the shops and enjoyed a bit of sightseeing. Elizabeth was showing signs of being her old self again, trying on different clothes and hats and generally having a good laugh with her daughter. On returning to the ship with several parcels they were both quite exhausted and in good spirits, looking forward to their next port of call, which was to be Melbourne. They arrived in Melbourne early on a Sunday morning and Elizabeth decided that they should attend church before going anywhere else. After church they strolled around the almost deserted streets and, with all the shops closed, decided that the rest of the time would be taken up with sightseeing.

As they continued on their leisurely walk, they passed a small church hall with one door slightly ajar and, after passing, Elizabeth suddenly stopped. 'What is it mother?', Edith asked, looking at her mother, slightly concerned. Elizabeth, turning, replied a little uncertainly, 'I really don't know. I just feel we should look in here', she said taking several steps back and looking in the door. Inside the compact little hall, there appeared to be a dull blue haze about the place with a small congregation, sitting quietly, listening intently to a medium speaking in a soft voice. Elizabeth, looking back at her daughter, said in a quiet voice, 'Come on Edith, let's sit in on this and see what's going on. It will pass a bit of time before going back to the ship'. With that, both women silently entered the back of the hall and, unseen by anyone, took a seat right at the very back. The medium, who had her eyes closed as she continued to speak softly during the proceedings suddenly stopped, and then sat bolt upright in her chair. With her eyes still closed, she raised her voice saying, 'I see a shipping disaster with great loss of life!'. Edith and her mother looked at each other, surprise on their faces, and then turned back to look at the medium, now looking up towards the ceiling. She went on, 'People are drowning and crying out for help!'. Lowering her face, eyes still closed and palms of her hands down on the table in front of her, she continued, 'I have strong feelings of someone wishing to communicate'. She stopped as though in deep thought and then went on, 'It is a man I think. Yes! It is a man wishing to communicate with someone close by'. Stopping briefly before going on, 'Someone very close by'. Again she cried out 'yes' and then said, 'It is so strong!'. By this time she was slightly trembling, 'It's someone here in this congregation with whom this person would like to communicate'.

Edith sucked in her breath as her mother looked on in utter astonishment at the medium as she continued saying, now with her eyes open, 'If there's anyone here that can identify with a shipwreck or people drowning, I would ask that they remain behind after this session this morning'. She went on, 'I am receiving such strong signals from the other side that I am sure I will have a message for them'. Elizabeth appeared to be stunned, her daughter, first looking at her mother and then back to the medium, just didn't know what to make of it all. After the seance had drawn to a close, people began to file out quietly as Elizabeth and her daughter remained seated at the back. Edith, leaning towards her mother, whispered, 'What does it all mean? What do you think is going to happen?'. Her mother replied softly, 'I don't know yet my dear, but I have a strong feeling that we should remain to hear what she has to say'.

Elizabeth was a religious woman and a great believer in life after death and had brought Edith up much the same way. She was intrigued by this woman and wanted to hear more. The medium, sitting at the small table at the front of the hall, stood up briefly and beckoned to them to come forward to join her. As they made their way to the front of the hall, she arranged two chairs for them at the table, before sitting down again. The medium was a portly woman of average height with a kindly face and greeted them warmly and asked them to take a seat. She began immediately by saying, 'This person really wants to get in touch with you. I can't remember feeling such a strong intercession'.

Placing both hands palms down on the table in front of her, she looked directly at Elizabeth and said in a shaky voice, her lips trembling, 'I am at this moment receiving extremely strong messages from an elderly man, possibly connected to a shipwreck'.

She went on in a louder voice, 'Your presence here brings it on in great strength'. She looked above their heads as though staring into space and went on, 'There are strong, yes, very strong indications for me to write something for you'. Her brow now showing signs of moisture as she continued, 'It is so strong! I must write something for you!'. Elizabeth and Edith were both mesmerised as she went on, shaking, her voice continuing to tremble as she said again almost trance like, 'I must write'.

Reaching across the table, her gaze still fixed at some imaginary point above their heads, she clumsily pulled a pencil and a scrap of paper towards her. She repeatedly said, 'It's so strong' and then began to move her hand shakily across the paper. There were a few loops and squiggles at first that meant nothing and then suddenly, her arm jerked. Elizabeth and Edith watched the medium's hand, their eyes glued to the paper, as she began to slowly write with more purpose. The pencil now moved across the paper, as it began to reveal the name 'Thomas Brown'. Elizabeth sat shaking like a leaf, staring at the beautiful copperplate handwriting that could only be that of her beloved Tom. Edith sat staring at the crumpled scrap of paper, her eyes riveted to her father's own unmistakable handwriting. Both women sat motionless, utterly spellbound, Elizabeth with tears in her eyes, her lower lip trembling. The medium went on, 'I am to tell you that he has not suffered in any way and that he and the Reverend Carter are together and at peace'. She smiled slightly, bringing her eyes down to meet theirs, saying finally, 'You are not to worry any more. He loves you dearly and will visit you tonight when you are asleep'.

On leaving the church hall, both women were visibly shaken by their experience with the medium. As they walked back along the quiet streets to their cruise ship, Edith said to her mother, 'How could a total stranger know so much about father?'. Elizabeth replied, 'It's extraordinary I know but when we were on our way to England on the Celtic and I mentioned to you how I preferred to stay in our cabin, well it was then that I had a feeling your father wanted to contact us . It was during that time that I could really feel his presence, especially around the area where the Titanic had gone down'. She then said to Edith, 'It's strange how things have worked out'. In what way mother?', replied Edith. Her mother said that it was almost as though they had been meant to take this trip.

She then added that Thomas had always believed that a person gets certain signs in life of which they should take notice. She finally said, 'When you consider that a sea cruise was advised and I went ahead with it, then don't you think that it was meant to happen, so that we could meet that one person who would put us in touch with your father?'. Edith replied, 'Knowing father, that's what he would have wanted. To put our minds at rest and if that's what's happened today, I think it's worked and it's all very wonderful'. Elizabeth, smiling to herself, thought how quickly Edith had grown up over this past year. That evening, after the ship had left Melbourne, both women were tired and opted for an early night. They both had a feeling of great inner happiness that they had never experienced before. As they lay in their berths and slowly drifted into a light sleep, Edith knew that her father had kept his promise as she felt a soft kiss upon her cheek. Her mother on the opposite side of the cabin, also sleeping lightly, smiled as she felt her beloved Thomas kiss her gently on the lips.

After the cruise had ended back in Capetown, Edith and her mother began to settle down again but it was not to be for long. Elizabeth expressed a wish to return to Johannesburg and, as she put it, wanted to do something with her life. She had been trained as a young woman in millinery and feather curling and felt that she would like to get back into it. They moved up to Johannesburg later that year and Elizabeth set about going into business on her own. Ostrich feathers were very fashionable at that time, being used in women's hats and costumes, and she could see a good market there for her skills.

As she was setting up her business, she became quite friendly with a young gentleman who was advising her on financial matters and on how to go about taking on this enterprise. However, after putting a great deal of effort into the business, along with a substantial amount of capital, it just wasn't making a profit and, several months later, Elizabeth had to abandon the idea and cut her losses. She heard from others that she had been ill advised and had taken on too much too quickly. Her young adviser disagreed and said that ostrich feathers were on the way out and that the venture would have been doomed to failure anyway unless they had diversified.

After the failure of her business venture, Elizabeth continued to see the young business adviser, much to Edith's annoyance. He would call on her quite regularly and take her out to dinner or out for the day, leaving Elizabeth to foot the bill most of the time. Edith, now 17 years of age, tried her best to like her mother's new companion but she just felt that he was wrong for her. Her father had been 20 years older than her mother, this man was 20 years her junior, the contrasts seemed too great. Her mother still had a considerable amount of money and, unfortunately, it was beginning to look to Edith that this was the main attraction for him. Elizabeth was showing a real zest for life and enjoyed his company and was always ready to go along with whatever plans he had. Edith knew that it would be a delicate subject to raise with her mother but she thought it her duty to try to get through to her before this man took her for every penny.

Sitting out on their verandah one evening, facing each other over a wicker table, Elizabeth told her daughter about the wonderful time she'd had the night before with Peter and his friends at a party. Edith then said, 'Don't you think he's a bit young for you, mother?'. Her mother replied, 'Yes, he is rather young but he is such fun and I think after the last couple of years, it's about time that I started to enjoy life again'. Edith wasn't going to let this go and so went on, 'He always seems to be short of money and is always borrowing from you'. Her mother replied, 'He means well. It's just that he's not very good at organising his own affairs that's all'. Edith went on, 'What kind of man will let you spend so much money on him and never offer to pay any of it back?'. Elizabeth leaned forward in her chair, and holding her daughter's hands in hers, said, 'Come now my dear, it's not as bad as all that, besides, have you ever thought of how much I enjoy spending money on Peter from time to time?'. Edith never knew that things had progressed like they had, and was beginning to feel that this whole conversation was becoming pointless. She finally said to her mother, 'Where will Peter be when the money has gone mother?'. This took Elizabeth by surprise, her daughter having never spoken to her this way before, but she knew deep down that she was concerned over her welfare. She also knew that Edith was now fast approaching womanhood, and was beginning to take after her with her outspoken views and opinions.

Edith, from that point onwards, no longer discussed her mother's relationship with Peter and did her best to avoid him. Her mother was clearly obsessed with the man and she knew that it didn't matter what she thought, nothing was going to change. Several months later, Elizabeth dropped the bombshell on her daughter by announcing that she and Peter were to marry. After the shock of hearing this, Edith made up her mind that she would try to show that she was happy for her mother and expressed her enthusiasm at the impending wedding. At night when in her bed however, Edith would weep silently when she thought of her dear father being replaced by this man who was his absolute opposite.

They married shortly after Edith's 18th birthday and her mother appeared to be so happy that Edith began to feel guilty at doubting her mother's judgment. Several months later though things began to change as Peter, now her stepfather, began to interfere more and more in her own private affairs. Edith, always to the point, would remind him that he was married to her mother and not her. Things came to a head one afternoon after Edith had arrived home after buying herself some new clothes. 'You're spending your money far too freely', he said to her as she went about unpacking her bags. He went on, 'You just don't seem to understand the value of money. 'Edith swung round to him and retorted, 'It's none of your business what I do with my own money!'. He then replied, in an attempt to sound fatherly, 'If you were my daughter, I would put you on a fixed allowance until you knew better'. Edith shot back at him, 'You're not my father. Thank God!'. And then feeling the anger rising in her, went on, 'The only reason you are here is to spend my mother's money and to satisfy your own drinking habits!'. And then raising her voice some more, she pointed her finger at him and said, 'Don't you ever forget that it's my fathers money that you are living off in the first place!'. With that, he mockingly bowed towards her and sneeringly replied, 'Then I take my hat off to your dear departed father', and then, straightening up, followed up with a rude gesture.

Edith exploded, lunging forward and slapping him as hard as she could across his face. This fury from such a small women took him utterly by surprise, knocking him off balance, causing him to almost fall over a chair close by. Quickly putting his hand up to his stinging face, he spun on his heel and stormed out of the room. This then ultimately caused an argument with her mother. Edith said to her mother, in no uncertain terms, that this man and his drinking habits would drag them both down until they had nothing left. Elizabeth hated having this argument as much as Edith, but she realised that her daughter was now a grown woman and perhaps the time had come for her to start making a life for herself. Elizabeth, waiting for Edith to calm down, finally said to her, 'You two are never going to get on are you?'. Edith replied, much more subdued, 'I'm sorry, mother. It's just that when he mentioned father and then made that rude gesture, I just lost control'. She then went on, 'Perhaps I can find somewhere else to live and it will make things easier for all of us'. Elizabeth, with complete understanding, then said to her daughter, 'You and I have been through a great deal together, Edith and the last thing I want is for you to leave over a silly argument with your stepfather'. She then went on, 'Perhaps, on the other hand, if you feel that's what you want to do to get on with your own life, then I won't stand in your way'. Edith replied in resignation, 'I just can't live under the same roof as that man, mother. I'm sorry. I shall just have to find somewhere else to live'. Elizabeth looked long and hard at her daughter before finally saying, 'I will always be here if ever you need anything, my dear'.

Edith moved out a week later to stay with a friend who had also just recently decided to leave her mother and go it alone. Kathryn van Rensburg had known Edith and her family from Capetown and the girls had been friends for years. Kathryn's father had been a close business associate of Thomas. Both women settled in well together and Edith was getting out and about much more, totally enjoying her new lifestyle. She would regularly visit her mother whenever she knew her stepfather wasn't going to be there and her relationship with Elizabeth was as close as ever.

HUWELIKSERTIFIKAAT.
MARRIAGE CERTIFICATE.

Revenue 210.

(*Uitgereik ooreenkomstig Artiekel 40 van Wet No. 17 van 1923.*)
(*Issued in terms of Section 40 Act No. 17 of 1923.*)

A 80744

Ras / Race: Man / Husband ——— Vrou / Wife ———

Huwelik bevestig op / Marriage solemnized at JOHANNESBURG Distrik / District JOHANNESBURG Provinsie / Province

Datum van Huwelik. Date of Marriage.	Volle Name van Eggenotes. Full Names of Persons Married.	Ouderdom. Age.	Geboorteland. Country of Birth.	Persoonlike staat. Personal Status.	Beroep. Occupation	Woonplek ten tyde van huwelik. Residence at time of Marriage.	Na gebooie of met spesiale Huweliks-lisensie. Banns or Special Marriage Licence.	Met wie se toestemming. Consent by whom Given.	Op of sonder huweliks-voorwaardes. With or without Antenuptial Contract.	Opmerkinge. Remarks.
30th June 1917	Frederick Thankful Haisman	22	England	Bachelor	–	[illegible]	Special Licence dd. Jhburg 30/6/17	own	without	no
	and									
	Edith Eileen Brown	20	Cape Province	Spinster	–	[illegible]		Mother. Father deceased		

Hierdie huwelik is deur my bevestig op hede die / This marriage was solemnized by me on this the 30 dag van / day of June 1917.

in die teenwoordigheid van ondergetekende getuies:— / in the presence of the undersigned witnesses:—

Predikant. / Minister.

Kerkgenootskap. / Denomination.

S.G. Mechie Magistraat. / Magistrate.

Getuies: / As witnesses:
1. M. Heathcote
2. A. Rice

Hierdie huwelik is voltrek tussen ons. / This marriage was contracted by us. F. Haisman / E. Brown

Ek, / I, J.H. Green sertifiseer hierby dat bostaande 'n getroue afskrif is van die „Originele Huweliksregister" in my kantoor gehou, van die huwelik tussen / do hereby certify that the above is a true copy of the Original Marriage Register kept in my office, of the marriage of Frederick T. Haisman en / and Edith E. Brown

Bekragtig deur my handtekening en seël op / Witness my hand and seal at JOHANNESBURG hede die / this 6th dag van / day of December 1938.

A copy of Edith and Fred's Marriage certificate.

On one of her visits, they briefly talked about her stepfather, with Elizabeth saying that the slap across his face made him realise that he had gone too far. Both women burst out laughing when Elizabeth said to Edith, 'You can certainly pack a punch!'.

It was now April 1917, and it was approaching the fifth anniversary of the sinking of the Titanic. At the Dance and Social Club that Edith and Kathryn attended on a regular basis, a competition was being organised for those interested in safety at sea. The main theme of the competition was for candidates to come up with their best ideas for saving lives from a shipwreck, with the Titanic in mind. Kathryn was well known by the club officials as a bit of a character, and she took it upon herself to elect Edith and Elizabeth as judges, along with two other nautical types. The club organisers jumped at the idea and it was arranged that, with the competition, they would hold a dinner and dance, turning the whole evening into a lot of fun. Elizabeth was thrilled at the idea and was really looking forward to it, her husband, however, preferring to go drinking with his friends in the wine bars in the city. Edith was quite pleased that he wouldn't be there.

On the evening of 15 April at the Dance and Social Club, before judging commenced, a short service was held for those that had perished on the Titanic. There had been a good response, with many interested people taking part and, once all the various ideas had been scrutinised, the judges, after much deliberation, had a winner. Edith, being the youngest judge, had the honour of handing over the prizes. The winner, whose blueprint was laid out in typical draughtsman-like style, had his name called out by the chairman. Amid wild applause, Fred Haisman came up to collect his prize from Edith, a silver plaque with 'Practical Ideas' inscribed across it and a space

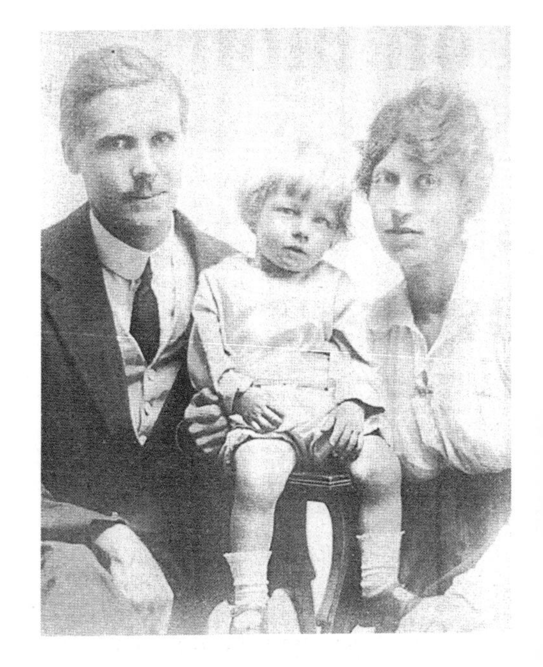

Fred, Fred jnr and Edith.

for his name to be engraved. On handing him his prize, Edith shook him by the hand. Fred thanked her and then, 'Perhaps you would like to join me for a glass of wine later?'. Edith, looking at him shyly and feeling her colour rising slightly, turned away from his gaze saying, 'I'm not one for drinking with strange men'. Fred laughed at that and went on, 'I agree with you entirely! That's why I'm asking you to join me. I'm not strange at all!'. Edith's colour continued to rise as she stammered, 'I I I'm with a friend anyway'. 'Fine', said Fred, 'Then bring her along as well and we can all celebrate together!'.

Once the meal was over and the tables cleared away for dancing, Edith said to Kathryn, 'Did you know what the winner said to me when I handed him his prize?'. 'No,' said Kathryn, now all ears, 'Do tell!'. Edith went on giggling, 'He only asked me to join him for a glass of wine, would you believe!'. Kathryn replied, full of fun as always, 'Cheeky little chappie, isn't he?'. They both burst out laughing as Kathryn continued, 'Watch out Little Miss Innocence. He's got his beady eye on you, I do declare'. With that they made their way out on to the verandah to join another group of their friends there.

Out in the night air on the verandah, Edith thought of Fred again and thought him good looking, with an air of confidence about him that was so attractive. As she and Kathryn chatted between themselves and with their friends, Fred moved up alongside her and said, 'As I'm no longer a stranger to you, how would you like the next dance?'. Edith started to laugh as he gently took her by the hand and led her onto the dance floor for an old-fashioned waltz. Edith felt flushed again but so pleased that he had come and asked her to dance. As they whirled around the floor she had never felt as happy as she was feeling right now and hoped that it would never end. For the rest of that evening they were inseparable, taking to the floor for almost every dance, Edith becoming quite breathless by it all. Elizabeth looked on, recognising the look on her daughter's face and feeling the happiness she felt.

Over the following weeks, Edith was to learn quite a lot about Fred and his family background. He was an engineering draughtsman and this was the reason that his exhibit for Safety as Sea was so professional when he presented his ideas. She was also beginning to find out about his dry sense of humour and, at times, he would have her in stitches with his off the cuff remarks. She was fascinated at his apparently wide knowledge about most things and would love listening to his views on many subjects.

His father, Frederick Haisman Senior, was also an interesting man, being a bit of an inventor and also building his own 'Velocopede' in 1873. He was an all-round sportsman and a champion cyclist and was a close associate of Dan Rudge and Thomas Humber, well known leading cycle manufacturers in England at that time. Frederick Haisman Senior was chairman of the Wemmer Pan sailing club and had served as Staff Sergeant in the South African Cycle Corp from 1900 to 1902, due to his involvement in the manufacture of the Safety Bicycle. This cycle was solely designed for military use, hence his position in the army. The Haisman family was originally from London.

Edith had known Fred for just six weeks when, one night over dinner, he proposed to her. She accepted and on 30 June 1917, they were married. It was to be a marriage that was to last for over 60 years. Shortly after their marriage, they bought their home in Johannesburg and life for Edith was blissfully happy. They had a wide circle of friends and a good social life, spending many hours sailing and, at the end of the day, enjoying cocktails and a meal at the sailing club. It was during this time that Fred set about building his own sailing boat and his yachting friends agreed that it was a fine boat when finished. Edith saw less of her mother after her marriage but she appeared happy enough each time she visited her. On one of her visits she noticed that her stepfather and mother were both a bit tipsy, which was a new development and something she had never seen in her mother before. The most she would ever drink would be perhaps a sherry before dinner in the evening. However, if her mother was happy then she had no intention of interfering, although the look she gave her stepfather on leaving left him in no doubt what she thought.

Some six months after her marriage, Edith became pregnant and her first son was born on the 9 August 1918. They were delighted with his arrival and they named him Frederick after his father. At birth he weighed in at just a little over three pounds, but was perfectly healthy despite that. Life began to change after the birth of Frederick Junior with all those sailing weekends having to take second place, until he became a little bit older. It was during this time that Fred and Edith began to discuss their future and, particularly, Fred's work prospects. Although they were well settled and loved Johannesburg, there just wasn't the kind of work that his profession called for, namely shipbuilding and dock construction work.

Chapter Twelve
Southampton

It was now 1920 and the past decade had seen historic events on a massive scale. The sinking of the Titanic eight years ago, would go down in history as one of the world's worst maritime disasters. Undeterred by the disaster, the British had built another huge liner for the North Atlantic trade, the largest in the world at the time, named the Aquitania. The past ten years had been mainly dominated by the Great War from 1914 to 1918 in which, it was estimated, in excess of ten million people lost their lives, a figure impossible to imagine. The war was madness, it was stalemate, it was futile. British troops played football with German troops on Christmas day. The next day they were back in their trenches shooting at each other. This had been the decade of the Russian Revolution, the Treaty of Versailles, the great engineering feat of the Panama Canal. Britain saw the emergence of the suffragette movement, the first non-stop Atlantic flight by Alcock and Brown, the name Charlie Chaplin appearing in cinemas. This decade was to bring to the world the rising power of America, with its increasing influence on the rest of the world and its powerful industrial base.

Edith was now 24 years of age. It was decided that they sell up and move to Southampton in England, in order for Fred to pursue his career as a draughtsman in docks' engineering and the shipbuilding industry. There was to be a huge dock-rebuilding program in Southampton, which would be of several years' duration. It was called the New Docks Scheme. Before leaving for England, Edith and Fred did the rounds, visiting their many friends. Some made the comment that they'd be back. Edith paid a visit to her very dear friend, Kathryn van Rensburg two days before their departure and found her madly in love with an Afrikaans farmer. 'I'm going to be a farmer's wife, have lots of kids and work the land', she said to Edith as they hugged each other on parting. Finally they said they would keep in touch no matter what. It was the last time she would ever see Kathryn as she died from septicaemia two years later caused by a ruptured appendix.

They went to see Elizabeth on their last day and it was a sad occasion with her hugging little Fred and crying. Edith promised her mother on leaving that she would write regularly and that they would be back when the dock contract had ended. Unknown to them both at the time, they would never see each other again. Edith and Fred sailed from Capetown on the Saxon, a Union Castle liner that they had both travelled on before and a ship they liked. On leaving Capetown, Edith discovered that she was pregnant again with her second child. As they left harbour, Edith looked back once again at Table Mountain and thoughts came flooding back to her. She remembered the last time she had left Capetown, supposedly for another country. She was a 15-year-old girl then with her mother and father embarking on an exciting new adventure - life in America. This time was different, she would be heading for a new life in England with her husband and son, with another on the way. Sitting up on deck on those warm tropical nights with Frederick Junior tucked up in his cot they would talk, among other things, about what the future had in store for them. Edith knew that her husband had the ability to get on in life and suggested that he attend night school once they had settled into their new home to increase his qualifications.

After nearly three weeks at sea, they docked in Southampton on a beautiful day in August at berth 46, the same berth that she and her mother had departed from eight years previously. Before disembarkation, Edith, with her husband, looked across the dock basin at berth 43. Fred said, 'That's where it all started for you Edith'. Staring across at the empty wharf she finally replied, 'Yes', and then added, 'I just hope that living in this town doesn't bring back too many memories that's all'. She then went on, 'This town must be full of widows from the Titanic. And then briefly forgetting her own sad loss, went on, 'They must have suffered dreadfully'. Fred standing alongside her, his arm around her waist, said, 'The English are good at picking up the pieces. They've had lots of practice'.

Edith's second son, Kenneth, was born in February 1921 and she was beginning to discover that life in England was going to be harder than she had first anticipated. Her upbringing in South Africa had been focused on her attaining a good education and then becoming 'a lady' who would marry well and have servants to help her run her household. This is what her parents wanted for her. Going out to work for a living or doing mundane jobs like housework was never a consideration. Most of the white population in South Africa had servants to do all the jobs involved with running a home and looking after children and it was expected that, when she had her own home, she would have that similar kind of lifestyle. However, it was not to be in England, with Edith having to acquire all those household chores totally unfamiliar to her - cooking, washing and ironing and scrubbing floors. She was also to learn on how to keep a cold and draughty home warm in the winter months on a tight budget.

Edith had learned a great deal about running a home from a neighbour of hers who also became a very good friend. Mrs Fisher taught her how to light coal fires without using wood and how to save partly burnt coals in the mornings when cleaning out the grate. She would clean the brasses around the fireplace and scrub the hearth, black-lead the cooking range once a week, and bake bread twice a week. She learned how to turn the collars and cuffs on Fred's shirts and how to starch. It was all a far cry from the cosseted life she had led in South Africa but Edith was a good pupil and had a determination to succeed in whatever the undertaking.

In February 1923, her third son Geoffrey was born, making it a busy time for Edith but, generally, life was good with Fred holding down a good job, something to be envied in those days. There were well over a million unemployed in the early 1920s, and some 350 000 of those were servicemen who had been lucky enough to have returned home alive from the Great War, but now unemployment was to be their reward. Edith had settled well into her housekeeping routine, keeping the home clean and tidy and herself, always clean and changed to greet her husband when he came home from work. Throughout these past four years, Edith had always kept in regular touch with her mother, although Elizabeth's letters were becoming less frequent as time went on. Those letters she did receive from her mother showed that she was reasonably happy, although her writing was now becoming untidy.

In January 1925 a fourth son was born and he was named Leo. After his birth it was decided to move to a larger house in Leighton Road, Sholing, a suburb of Southampton. It was during this time that Fred started going to night school, Edith being the main architect behind that. She was the driving force behind her husband always maintaining that he should not let a growing family deter him from pursuing his career prospects. From late 1925, letters from Elizabeth to Edith were becoming fewer and far between causing Edith to be concerned about her mother's welfare. Her mother's handwriting was becoming worse, although her letters gave no indication that anything was wrong.

Edith had never liked or trusted her stepfather and, at times, wondered just what kind of life he was giving her. During the first week in July, Edith received a letter from her stepsister to say that Elizabeth had died in hospital in Salisbury, Rhodesia from sclerosis on the 29 June 1926, aged just 53. Edith felt that her mother and father were together again, her mother never ever getting over the loss of her beloved Thomas. Early in 1927, Edith found that she was pregnant again and for some considerable time they had hoped that they would eventually have a girl. Their wish had finally been granted when, in July that year, Edith finally gave birth to a daughter, and such was their delight they decided to call her Joy. In October 1929, Edith gave birth to her sixth child, another boy, and they named him John. Edith was well now occupied in bringing up her large young family, although large families were commonplace in those days so she was no different to anyone else in that respect. It was, nevertheless, hard work and she coped extraordinarily well, raising the children to have good manners. She was always being the main disciplinarian in the home.

As 1930 approached there was little said about the Titanic disaster other than it had taken place and the history books said it was one of the world's worst disasters in maritime history. Edith only spoke about it when prompted by someone, or asked by one of her children, but other than that it had been laid to rest. The past decade had seen many changes throughout the world, the 1920s being recognised as the start of the 'Jazz' age, with its Charleston and outrageous fashions. For those with a job, life was good. Alexander Fleming had discovered penicillin and insulin, discoveries that would save millions of lives in years to come. John Logie Baird had taken the first tentative steps towards producing the first television pictures. From America came never-ending movies of Chaplin, Rudolph Valentino and Douglas Fairbanks Junior. However, throughout Europe, things were beginning to fester with men like Mussolini, Stalin and Hitler thrusting their ruthless ideals on the masses. The end of this decade saw the Wall Street crash and the beginnings of the Great Depression.

During the early part of the 1930s, the Cunard Line began to move their ships down to Southampton from Liverpool and as a result, many crew members made their homes in the port. One of those was Captain Rostron of the Carpathia who went on to command other ships of the line until his retirement. If it had not been for his immediate response to the Titanic's distress calls, the loss of life would have been almost total. He was rightfully looked upon by many as a hero. In March 1932, Edith gave birth to their seventh child, another girl, and she was named Dorothy after Edith's little sister, who had tragically died in 1908. With such a large family, life for Edith was very restricted, leaving her little time for anything other than raising her children. The Great Depression was having its effect on everyone and, although Fred managed to keep in full employment, poverty could be seen everywhere.

With so many children to look after, feeding and clothing them was a major operation. At the end of each day when they were all in bed, Edith's relaxation was to sit by the fire, patching and sewing, darning socks and making alterations to clothes for hand-me-downs to save money on clothing. There was a never-ending stream of kids at her elbows, looking for that little bit over as she baked and cooked and forever searched for ways to make ends meet. She would wonder at times how those families were coping with their fathers out of work when she knew how much of a struggle it was with Fred in work.

In 1933, Frederick Junior joined the Royal Navy at the age of 15, going off to St Vincent's training college at Portsmouth. It was in this year that work started on the largest ocean-going liner ever built, the 81 000-ton liner, Queen Mary, a ship almost twice the size of the Titanic. Quite clearly the British had decided that big ships were here to stay and many lessons had been learned. This massive ship would cruise across the North Atlantic at 33 knots with well over 3000 people on board during peacetime. It was at this time that the Georgic and Britannic were the last ships to be built for White Star Line and, by 1934, the company had amalgamated with the Cunard Steamship Company, later to be known as the Cunard White Star Line.

By 1934, Edith had given birth to her eighth child, another son and he was named Donald. Living at this time in Spring Road, Sholing, Southampton, Edith gave birth to two more sons, Brian in 1937 and her last child, David in 1938. This then was to be the complete Haisman family comprising eight sons and two daughters. If her mother and father had been alive, they would never have believed it.

On the 3 September 1939, Britain and France declared war on Germany and, within hours of that declaration, air raid sirens could be heard in England for the first time. This was now causing concern to all families with sons and daughters who were at an age for military service. Fred and Edith had four sons who would be serving in the war and that in itself was worrying, but other families were in the same situation and they just had to live with it. There was the added concern of being bombed out of house and home for those that remained at home. Southampton was a strategic target for the Luftwaffe, with its docks and shipyards and Supermarine seaplane base and was frequently subjected to heavy bombing raids. Fred Senior became an Air Raid Warden and would be out most nights ensuring blackout regulations were adhered to whilst Edith remained at home with the younger children.

One of the safeguards during bombing raids was keeping the younger children bedded down under the tables downstairs. Although bombs could be dropped anywhere in the neighbourhood, the facts remained that many people were injured from falling plaster and masonry from adjacent hits, perhaps several streets away. Once Edith had made sure that the children were tucked away into their little 'havens', she would then go upstairs to sleep alone as Fred was out all night on warden duty. She always maintained that Hitler would never keep her out of her own bed, whatever the outcome. During air raids several neighbours always made for Edith's house for a bit of a chat to try to take their minds off the bombing. She was always pressed by them to tell them stories about the Titanic and her life as a young girl living in South Africa. They found comfort from these stories and, being together when these air raids were going on, felt a kind of security whilst their menfolk were away fighting the war.

Late one night during an air raid, there was a direct hit on the railway viaduct at the bottom of their road and, as a result, the blast blew all the windows out of most houses in the neighbourhood. There was glass everywhere but as luck would have it, none of the children was injured. Edith quickly came downstairs and calmed all the children down and then organised them all to sleep upstairs for the rest of the night. She then set about the task of clearing away all the broken glass spread throughout the house as the children went back to sleep. It was her courage that made people feel secure when they were around her and she always did a good job of never showing her fear. Deep down though, she had the same fears as everyone else. With Fred away most nights, her only help was her eldest daughter, Joy who, at the age of 14, was a tremendous help to her, especially with the younger children. Unfortunately, Joy became a real worry for Fred and Edith when she mysteriously contracted polio and spent over six months flat on her back in an iron lung in a hospital in Alton in Hampshire.

Most of these air raids were at night but as the war progressed the Germans decided that daytime air raids were also necessary as Britain was becoming a tougher nut to crack than they had first realised. During these heavy bombing raids, both of Edith's youngest sons, Brian and David, were in hospital for hernia operations. While Brian was in the South Hants Hospital, part of the building took a direct hit, leaving his bed covered in broken glass just after his operation, leaving the little boy shell shocked. He was never to fully recover from that experience, perhaps being the only real war casualty the family had.

In 1939, Fred's father died in Johannesburg at the age of 80 and the Cape Times ran an article on his pioneering days in cycle manufacture. His involvement with the 'bone shaker', the Velocopede and the Safety Bicycle, designed for military use, were all topics of the article. By the end of 1940, Fred was working for the Admiralty in Portsmouth Dockyard and, with the continuing bombardment of the docks and naval bases, it was advised that many personnel be moved away to Chichester. This was a small very old township on the South Downs with no military establishments to speak of and would not pose any threat from German bombers.

As 1940 approached, the last ten years had seen millions unemployed throughout Europe and the United States. The threat of war was everywhere, in Spain, Africa, China, Japan and in Europe. In Germany, the world was to witness the rise of the Nazi Party, the persecution of the Jews and finally, genocide. Stalinist Russia saw the extermination of people on a par with Nazi Germany. The beginning of World War II was said to be, by many commentators, the war that had to happen. The 1930s had been a decade of human misery and suffering, with the deaths of millions of innocent people.

Once Fred's office had moved to Chichester, he made arrangements for Edith and the children to move out there away from Southampton and the never-ending air raids. Fred managed to purchase a cafe in a village called West Wittering, with a population of around 50 people, the rest made up of several farm animals. The village pub was called the Old House at Home and that was about as far as the entertainment went. The cafe was called the Cherries Cafe and was supported mainly by French Canadian troops stationed nearby and, although rationing made everything scarce, Edith, with the help of her daughter managed to cater quite well, considering.

The Empire Grace.

When living in Southampton it was suggested that the children be evacuated to outlying country districts for their safety, which would have meant Edith being separated from the children for long periods. She wasn't happy with that and by moving to West Wittering, it turned out to be the best solution for all concerned. By the end of 1941, the Japanese had bombed Pearl Harbour bringing the Americans into the war. One evening, Fred arrived home from work and said to Edith, 'Sit down. I've got some good news for you'. Edith, pulling a chair out from under the table, sat down thinking that good news was something you didn't hear much of these days. Fred said to her, 'The Admiralty have listed some overseas postings and one of them is a naval base called Simonstown, which isn't far from Capetown'. Edith's heart leaped for an instant and she was finding it difficult to contain her excitement as Fred went on, 'I've put in for that posting and, at the moment, no one else has shown any interest so I think we're in with a good chance'.

Edith was overjoyed at the prospect of returning to South Africa and getting the children away from war-torn Britain. She quickly asked Fred, 'How long do you think it will be before they will let you know?'. Fred, looking at his wife and the excitement showing in her face, went on with a smile, 'Knowing the Admiralty, and the way they work, it could be anyone's guess'. Fred went on, 'I don't think it will be too long because they will be closing the office down and moving part of our operations to Plymouth'. He continued, 'As you know, all these things are always carried out in the utmost secrecy and when it does come off, there will only be a few days to get organised before leaving'. He finally added, 'There's only one big drawback and that is, I shall be going first and it could be several months before you and the children will be able to follow'. Edith thought about that for a while before saying, 'It's a small price to pay if it means getting the children away from here until the war ends'. And then finally, 'And God knows when that will be'.

A further six weeks went by until Fred had confirmation that his posting had been accepted, with his departure details being withheld until closer to the time. On his way home that night he managed to get hold of a bottle of sherry and said to Edith, 'I'm on my way. Let's celebrate!'. Edith was so excited by it all knowing that at long last their luck was changing for the better. Several weeks passed without any further word from the Admiralty until 18 October when he received his sailing date. It was to be in five days' time, sailing out of Liverpool on a French ship which turned out to be a floating disaster. After various mishaps on board with crew trouble, the ship finally ran aground in Capetown, some six weeks after leaving Liverpool.

With her husband now in South Africa, Edith and the children just had to sit it out and wait as the war went on unabated and they also had to wait for the Admiralty to contact her. It was a trying time for her having never been separated from her husband in over 26 years of marriage. There was the added worry of the elder sons all away on active war service. She wrote to them all once a week and always seemed to be waiting for mail from overseas, and forever concerned about their safety. During this time, Geoffrey arrived home on survivor's leave after being bombed and torpedoed at sea. She also received a letter from a Commanding Officer in Alexandria to say that their eldest son, Frederick Junior was missing in action. Edith went through agony and torment again, much the same as she had experienced when her father was missing all those years ago when the Titanic went down.

It was nearly two weeks later when she heard that he had escaped from a prisoner of war camp and was now safe. It was just another waiting game with Edith never showing the children the real stress she was under from time to time. In January 1944, Edith finally heard that their passage had been arranged but the exact details were to be kept secret until their departure date. 'At long last!', exclaimed Edith when she read the letter. 'I thought they had forgotten us.' It had been over a year since Fred had left and apart from becoming fed up with it all, Edith never thought that it was going to take this long.

When their sailing instructions finally arrived several weeks later, they revealed that they would have to travel to Swansea to join a troop ship called the Empire Grace. She was a vessel, built by Harland and Wolfe of 13 473 tons, capable of a top speed of 17 knots and originally built for the Australian and New Zealand service and owned by the Shaw Savill Line. She was now in the hands of the British Government for troop-carrying purposes, with accommodation for just a few passengers. On arrival in Swansea on a frosty night in February, Edith and her six children went into lodgings for the night in preparation for joining the ship in the early hours of the following morning.

After sailing just before daybreak, they went up through the Irish Sea to Greennock on the west coast of Scotland. From here, the Empire Grace joined her convoy and, with 500 troops on board to be disembarked at St Helena, headed for the North

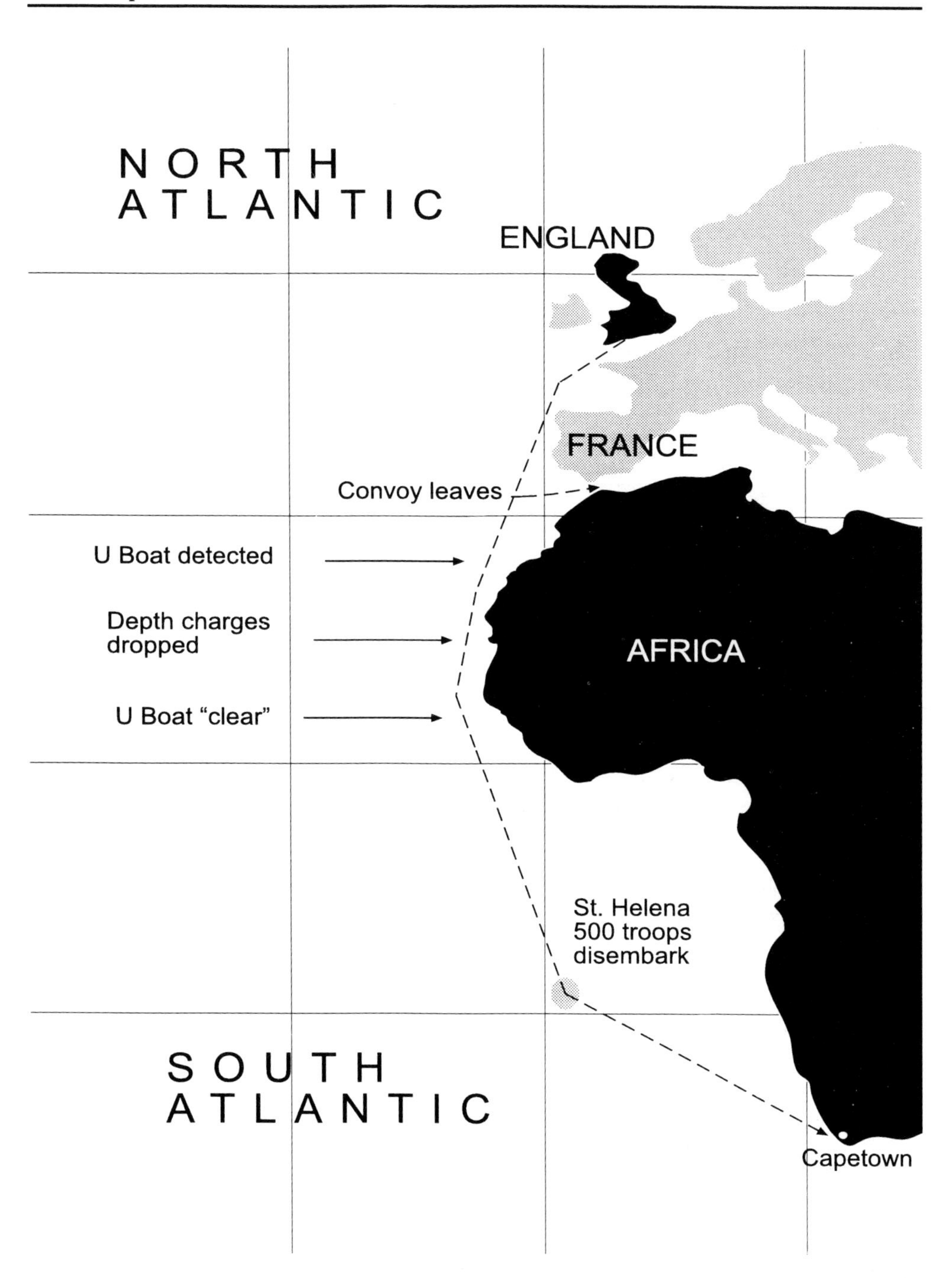

The Atlantic voyage to Capetown.

Atlantic. Once again, Edith found herself back at sea again, this time with six of her own children to keep her company. There were three other families on board, travelling under similar circumstances and everyone soon became friends, the children becoming favourites with the troops. Every child on board had been designated to a soldier in case of an emergency and this in itself was reassuring to parents. There had been considerable U-boat activity in the North Atlantic throughout the war and it was not unknown for submarines to patrol the South Atlantic as well. The Empire Grace, with her troops on board, would no doubt be a valuable target for German submarines, but the War Department considered that a convoy as far as the approaches to the Mediterranean, would be enough protection. After that, they would be on their own with two AA guns and depth charges.

The convoy left them during the night and on coming up on deck in the morning, most of them remarked on how lonely and vulnerable they felt when looking out on an empty sea. They continued to steam south, completely blacked out at night, with all the children being put to bed at night with as much clothing on as possible. Just 24 hours after leaving the convoy, they picked up a U-boat shadowing them as they approached the bulge of Africa. The whole vessel was on 'action stations' for the next several days, with depth charges being dropped at certain intervals as the submarine continued to follow them. It was during this emergency procedure that everyone would sit on the deck outside their cabins with life jackets on waiting for further instructions. Edith would sit for hours with the children, doing her knitting and telling them stories, the other few women on board, seeking out her company, and joining in. Inside, Edith was terrified at the thought of another shipwreck, this time with six of her own children.

Chapter Thirteen
Simonstown

As they sailed further into the South Atlantic, the threat of U-boats lessened. Three weeks after leaving Greenock, they dropped anchor off of St Helena. This was a small island under British rule, just ten miles long, of volcanic origin and lying 1700 miles from Capetown. This was the island Napoleon had been sent to in exile and he had eventually died there. The population, in 1944, was a little over 4500 and they now had an extra 500 British troops to protect them.

After the troops had disembarked and the children had tasted some fruit they had never seen before, they weighed anchor and headed for Capetown. On arrival in Table Bay, Edith looked towards Table Mountain and began to unwind. They had finally made it, and now the excitement was beginning to return at the thought of seeing Fred again after such a long year apart. Looking up at the mountain with its 'table cloth' draped over its top made Edith realise just how much she had missed this place. She took it all in, the colours, the small shantytowns at its base and Lion's Head, also known as Signal Hill, standing proudly alongside of the mountain. Capetown was known as the Mother City and also as Kaapstad to the Afrikaners. The memories came flooding back to her from the last time she was here. She had had a young son then and had said goodbye to her mother, not knowing she would never see her again.

Now she was back, away from the war in England and, ahead of them, was a much brighter future, especially for the children. Down on the dockside, Edith and the children were soon reunited with Fred, with lots of excitement and everyone talking at once. Edith, looking her husband up and down, laughingly said, 'You've put on a lot of weight, Fred! Perhaps it's time to give the brandy a rest!'. Fred laughing along with her replied, 'I've no idea what you're talking about!'. 'Besides', he said, changing the subject, 'We'd better hurry. We've got a train to catch'.

As the train headed for Simonstown, the children were full of excitement, looking out of the windows at the beautiful coastline and beaches, sights they had never set eyes on before. Every time the train sounded its siren, everyone would laugh, the sound being identical to an air raid siren back in England, and now a thing of the past. Simonstown was a pretty little township, situated on the side of a mountain, overlooking Simons Bay. It was named after Simon van der Stel, the Dutch governor in 1679, who was also responsible for naming Stellenbosch, a small town outside of Capetown.

Living in Simonstown made it difficult to believe there was a war on, life being good for all age groups and the children receiving a good education at the local school. Standards were high, the Afrikaans teachers strict and the Afrikaans language part of the curriculum. The three elder sons serving in the Royal Navy were fortunate enough to all get postings to Simonstown Naval Base. The fourth son, Leo, serving in the Merchant Navy in Russian convoys, also managed to get a ship to South Africa and, for once briefly, the whole family was together for almost a week. During the five years that Edith and her family lived in Simonstown, they were without doubt some of the happiest years of her life. They lived in a huge Admiralty house with a servant, the standard of living high and the children healthy with wonderful outdoor activity to keep them occupied. There was mountain climbing, fishing, never-ending parties and lazy days spent on the beaches. It was indeed a good life.

In that period, right up until 1948, the country was governed by General Smuts, viewed by the Afrikaners as being pro-British but nevertheless, the country was stable and the black people got on well with white. There was segregation between the groups but it was far more relaxed than the Apartheid regime that took over power in 1948, led by Dr Malan. By the middle of 1948, Fred's posting was coming to an end and with it so were the good times, on which they looked back on fondly for many years afterwards.

Their passage had been booked for them to return to Southampton in September of that year, sailing on the Pretoria Castle on her maiden return voyage. She was one of two 'super' liners built by Hartland and Wolf for the Union Castle Line to consolidate their monopoly over the South African-British trade. Life had never been easy in England for them, even during the so-called 'good times' and Edith and Fred knew that life wasn't going to be any picnic now that the war was over. Edith, as resilient as ever, never complained and faced up to the challenges that lay ahead. Their five-year stay in Simonstown had seen several changes in their family, with Geoffrey and Joy marrying while out there and Leo marrying back in England. The four youngest children had all developed South African accents and could converse in Afrikaans.

Edith was now 52 and once again they would be starting all over again in battle-scarred England. They weren't to know just how difficult it was going to be trying to find somewhere to live with five children. After two weeks at sea, they arrived back in Southampton to find the city heavily bombed, with ruins, derelict buildings and empty streets everywhere. There was nowhere to stay other than with their son Leo, his wife and two children who lived in a 'prefab'. These small prefabricated homes were designed to ease the housing shortage in the short term and were meant to house a family of five at the most. With Edith, Fred and the five children moving in with them, there was no less than 12 of them sharing that compact little home. Alternative accommodation had to be found and they spent all day and every day trudging the streets in search of accommodation.

In parkland, in the centre of Southampton, there was an American camp of almost 100 Nissen huts that had been vacated at the end of the war. The local authority decided that they would use these huts to help with the housing shortage and it was here that Edith and her family finally ended up. The rooms inside these huts were partitioned off with a metre gap at the top, and the main room had a circular stove in the middle with a chimney pipe running up through the roof. The whole place was known to be a slum throughout Southampton and a good place of which to steer clear. They were to remain here for two years and, at times, Edith would weep at the way her life had turned round once more, always for the worse it seemed. They all hated the place and Fred sent off many letters to try to get something better, but it was all to no avail, there just wasn't anywhere else to live

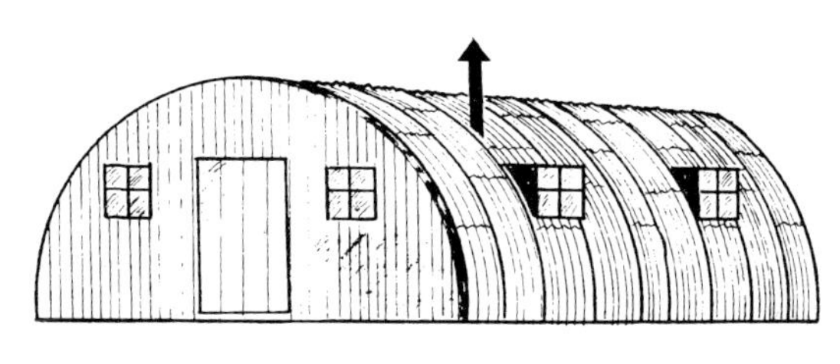

An illustration of a Nissen Hut where Edith and her family lived for 2 years.

at that time.

The neighbourhood comprised many gipsy families and travellers, a nomadic type, never settling anywhere. There were drunken fights and thieving, with women fighting each other and ripping their clothes off in public view. The police knew most of them by their first names and prostitutes lived and worked there. A prostitute was murdered there one night, her body being dragged to the middle of the cricket pitch. The next day local kids were picking up blood stained leaves and shoving them in match boxes for souvenirs. There were 'brick' raids at night. These consisted of the local youths heaving as many bricks as possible on to the corrugated roofs to try to get the occupants to give chase. When those bricks rained down on one's roof, it sounded like World War Three had just started. Many of the local lads ended up in Borstal institutions, their fathers in jail. It was a good place to get out of, and those two years were like an eternity for Fred and Edith.

During their stay at the huts in Southampton, Edith's second youngest son, Brian, was becoming too much for her to handle. Since his bombing experience in hospital as a child, he had never really picked up mentally and had also suffered a glandular problem, causing him to be excessively overweight. He would at times show extreme fits of anger and would wander off leaving everyone looking for him. At the age of 13 he was twice the size of Edith and was often incontinent. She had been advised many times to have him put into care where he would be looked after, but she wouldn't have any of her children taken away from her. Without a doubt, however, as he got older, he became too much for her and, eventually, she gave in and he was finally taken into care. She would visit him every week and spend hours with him taking all his favourite things and she began to think that it was the right thing to do after all. He appeared to have settled there and was doing well when suddenly, and without warning, he passed away one night from heart failure. Edith was devastated as she had nursed that boy all his life and for it to end abruptly like this, left her in a state of shock for a long time. He was a beautiful boy and dearly loved by everyone.

At long last, notice came through from the local authority that a new home had been found for them in Bitterne, a suburb of Southampton. Relief was felt by everyone and no one could get out of those huts quickly enough and start living in a real house again. They were to settle in no. 64 Yeovil Chase for the next 15 years during which time the remaining children all left school and pursued their own lifestyles. John and Donald joined the Royal Air Force and David, the youngest, the Merchant Navy, all of them realising that they would have to join one force or another with conscription still in force.

The 1940s had seen the end of World War II and the forming of the United Nations. India had become independent after 160 years of British rule. The loss of life over the past ten years as a result of the war was staggering. Russia alone had lost 20 million, Germany and Poland, 5 million each and 6 million Jews had died. There were massive losses in other countries and it was impossible to imagine what the total figure would be. It had been the decade of the 'Iron Curtain' and the 'Cold War'. The last ten years had witnessed a new horror, that of the atom bomb and the destruction of Hiroshima. The 1940s were the beginning of the nuclear age. The last ten years had shown that mankind had found bigger and better ways to wipe out their species.

After their move to the new house, life improved for Edith and her family and at last she could get a decent home together again. Fred had left the Admiralty and had joined Thorneycrofts Shipyard in Southampton as a draughtsman. The long spell of rationing had finally ended in 1954 and, for a while, everyone went mad eating chocolates and confectionary, Edith's favourite pastime. Things were slowly beginning to improve all round with all the children grown up, earning money, and off their hands.

The end of the 1950s had seen more wars, this time they were in Korea and Vietnam and the British had their Suez Canal crisis. There was also trouble for the British in Cyprus and Africa. The death of Stalin and the emergence of the arms race were also features of the decade. It appeared to be the time of the master spies with Maclean, Philby, Burgess and the Rosenburgs. It was a period when the first Hydrogen bomb was tested. It was also the decade when the first kidney transplant took place and the first computer was marketed.

On 17 July 1962, the premier showing of the film, A Night to Remember was being shown at the Odeon Cinema in Southampton and Edith, along with other Titanic survivors, was invited to attend. It was a fitting venue for this film as Captain Rostron of the Carpathia had opened this cinema back in 1937. Among those that attended that evening were Bert Dean, Eva Hart, Milvina Dean and Fred Fleet, the Titanic's lookout man who sadly later committed suicide after falling on hard times. Navigating officers from the Titanic, who may well have been expected to command their own ships in years to come, never achieved their goals. Shipping companies considered it bad publicity to have one of their ships commanded by an ex-Titanic officer. These men would have to live with this for the rest of their sea-going careers.

Life continued to be good for Edith and Fred throughout the 1960s and they were probably as happy now, as they had ever been in their long married life together. The 'swinging sixties' as they were known, were upon them with mini-skirts, flower power, flares and caftans. There were the Beatles and the Rolling Stones. The space race was on at this same time and the threat of nuclear war had never been closer. Apart from taking little notice of all of this, Fred was fast approaching retirement and was showing signs of becoming restless.

Chapter Fourteen
Australia

Fred finally retired from his work at Thorneycrofts Shipyard and was toying with the idea of joining his son and daughter who had emigrated to Australia just a few years previously. He had said to Edith that, now he had retired, they would have nothing to lose by the move, but Edith was reluctant to give up another home. However, Edith was from the 'old school' and stood by her husband in all things and finally she agreed, although she didn't consider it a wise move at their age. It can be said that Edith had suffered in silence on many occasions but was, for all of that, a loyal wife, a good mother and would always go with the flow regarding her family.

In December 1964, Edith and Fred sailed from Southampton on the P&O liner Oriana, arriving in Brisbane on 14 January 1965. On their arrival, they were met by the family already living out there and they received quite a bit of publicity due to Edith's connection with the Titanic. They finally settled in Highgate Hill, joining other members of the growing family already there. Brisbane was a fine city, which was rapidly going through change with the faithful old trams, being replaced with a faster and more efficient transport system. There were wonderful botanical gardens, parks and bird life in abundance, coupled with a good sub-tropical climate. Brisbane was a city on a par with the best in the world and situated on the winding Brisbane River; it was indeed a good place to live.

Edith and Fred before departing for Australia in 1964.

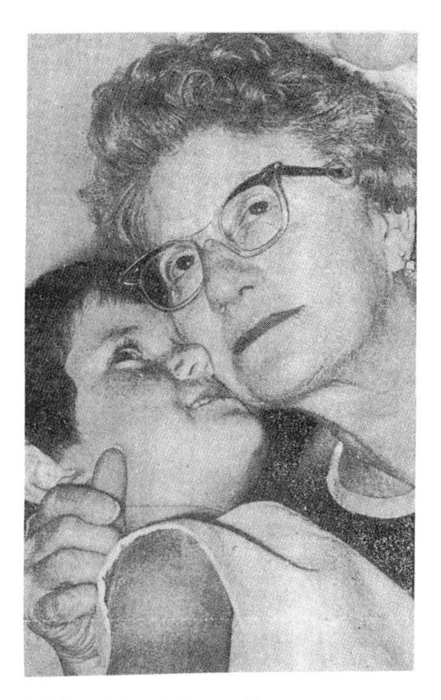

Edith arriving in Australia, greeted by Granddaughter Dawn. By courtesy of The Courier-Mail.

All the family had settled well until one of the grandchildren developed leukaemia and Edith's youngest son, David decided to take his son back to England in the hope that treatment there might save his life. It wasn't to be, with the boy dying 18 months later. This tragedy was to repeat itself when another son, Donald also lost his son from the same disease some seven years later. After eight years in Australia, Fred had decided that he wanted to return to England and Edith was expecting it, knowing her husband the way she did. Fred had a particularly conservative outlook on life and, ultimately, there was no place like England. Australia could have been the country they may well have settled in, but Fred decided that the Old Country was the place to spend the remainder of their days, despite the hard times it had put them through. They arrived back in Southampton in the winter of 1969 on a bitterly cold day in the middle of a power strike. Edith was now aged 74 with Fred two years her senior and together they both had to start all over again. They stayed with their son David until finally finding a flat in Westwood Road, Portswood, which by coincidence, was the next road to Winn Road where Captain Smith of the Titanic had lived.

Return to Southampton

The flat that Fred and Edith occupied was warden controlled leaving them quite settled and contented. They had their regular stream of visitors from family and friends and Saturday mornings usually saw a good gathering with a glass of sherry or two. As regards to the Titanic it was just a memory, with no one ever speaking about it and hardly any publicity other than when a survivor had passed on. Fred was once asked about it when in his local pub one evening and had replied, 'It looks as though the old girl has finally been laid to rest'. Whenever Edith spoke about the disaster she would always mention those hundreds of people crying for help as they drowned in that freezing ocean. Throughout her life she always said the same thing to all of those around her, 'I shall never forget those sounds as long as I live'.

In 1977, Fred and Edith celebrated their diamond wedding anniversary at Rhinefield House in the New Forest. Rhinefield House was a beautiful stately home in the heart of the forest and, although privately owned, part of it could be hired for special occasions. It was a grand occasion with all the family and relations as far afield as Australia, attending the function, dining in medieval style with jugs of mead and glasses of wine being brought by serving wenches in front of roaring log fires. It was a celebration worthy of a couple who had been married for 60 years, had had ten children and had travelled across the world together. It was an unforgettable evening with the press running the story and mentioning, of course, Edith's Titanic experiences. A tree was planted for them in the grounds of their flats where they lived, with the Lord Mayor of Southampton attending and later a party was held for the residents there.

Edith presented with her father's watch.

Some five months after their anniversary, Fred became ill and Edith, as usual, was determined that she would look after him even though it was far too much for her. He eventually was taken to hospital, an experience completely new to him having never been to hospital before and, shortly after being admitted, suffered a stroke and passed away on 26 November. Edith was heartbroken, having lost her partner of 60 years and, although her family did their best to console her, they were never to know the grief she felt. She was now 81 years of age and would face the time left to her, alone in her flat at Portswood. She was always a strong-willed woman and remained physically independent for as long as possible, only requiring from her family, those very important regular visits. On the 5 December 1980 Edith was to learn of the death of her eldest son, Frederick Junior in London. He had died from heart disease aged just 62.

It was now the end of the decade and the 1970s had seen many hijackings of airliners and hostages taken from all over the world. It was a decade of international terrorism. America was enduring Watergate and the Vietnam War was becoming a bigger embarrassment for the US the longer it went on. The last ten years had seen Britain finally join the Common Market. In 1981 serious attempts were being made to search the depths of the North Atlantic to find the sunken wreck of the Titanic Edith, when told by her son, David what was going on, replied, 'They'll never find it. She's gone forever'.

Searches by the US Navy continued in the area, mainly because they wanted to try out new submersible equipment in great depths of water. By 1984, the Americans had teamed up with the French and carried out further extensive searches in a large area thought to be where the ship had gone down. On 1 September an echo was received by sounding gear, believed to be that of a boiler casing. After further sweeps in the area it was confirmed that, after 72 years, the Titanic had finally been found.

The location of the wreck some two miles below the surface caused a great deal of excitement and enormous public interest. When her son, David asked her what she thought about this latest discovery, she replied, 'What on earth are they going to do with it?'. His reply at that time was, 'I should think it's far too deep to do anything with, mother'. 'That's good then', she replied, and she said that the dead should rest in peace. Unfortunately, that was not to be. The finding of the wreck began to stir up

Edith and Fred on board Oriana on voyage to Australia 23.12.64

ideas in those who could see some advantages. The quiet life that Edith had enjoyed over the past few years was about to change dramatically as some people began to view her with a renewed interest. Gone were those little chats from time to time with friends and relatives about the Titanic, now they wanted her autograph and more and more people were seeking her out to get her to sign scraps of paper or anything that could be written on.

Doctor Robert Ballard, heading the expedition, had said that the ship was lying in 13 000 feet of water, in total darkness and at peace. On discovery of the vessel, they held a service on board for those that had perished at this place 72 years ago. A brass plate was placed on the Titanic in memory of those that had lost their lives and Dr Ballard was of the opinion that she should remain at peace, the way she had been for all those years. When Edith had heard about this she felt comforted to know that the dead were being respected.

In the month of August 1985 Edith was to learn of the death of her son John from cancer, aged just 54. He had always led a healthy lifestyle and it came as a shock to everyone. By 1986 a further expedition was carried out on the Titanic site and manned dives in a submersible were made on the wreck. On several of these dives, a small remote-controlled pod, fitted with cameras, was operated from inside of the submersible and, for the first time in 74 years, the inside of the Titanic could be seen. There were to follow amazing pictures of wreckage and the ship's fittings scattered about the ocean floor, the ship itself almost on an even keel, its bow buried deep in the mud. The stern section lay almost a half a kilometre away from the forward section, confirming that the ship did break her back and parted just below the surface on sinking. As the vessel sank to the depths some two miles down, the two sections of her hull would have further separated during sinking and accelerated, as the air continued to be expelled.

The appearance of the two sections on the ocean floor would suggest that the bow section would have struck the seabed first at an angle, burying itself almost up to the anchors in the mud. As a result of this impact, plates on either side of the forward section were buckled and split and the mast and crow's nest were found to be lying across the bridge front. The stern section may well have hit the ocean floor 'flatter' and with great impact, as all the decks in that section had collapsed, one inside the other, the whole scene one of total destruction. Some pictures have shown that her huge reciprocating engines and cylinders had come off better, standing almost upright amidst the wreckage. Between the two sections of the Titanic lay a huge debris field with numerous pieces of crockery, deck fittings, suitcases, the odd safe, bottles of wine and large quantities of coal from the ships bunkers.

Brass fittings around the portholes, windows, the tops of capstans and around the bridge area had stood up well to the test of time, showing little sign of corrosion, but all wooden fitments had long since disappeared. Quite surprisingly, leather goods and some footwear also stood up well, as did clothing found in suitcases brought up on deck to the salvage vessels. For those carrying out the restoration work, it was no doubt an exciting time but there were many relatives who thought that all of these things should have been left well alone. There was never any sign of human remains, as first thought, but this was probably due to the great pressure and the organisms that will eventually destroy everything that was once Titanic.

On 15 April 1987 was the 75th anniversary of the sinking of the Titanic and Edith, along with the last few remaining survivors, were flown out to America to attend an 'Historical Titanic Convention'. It was also during this year that no less than 2000 items were retrieved from the wreck including, Thomas's gold pocket watch taken from a black Gladstone bag along with over 60,000 dollars inside. As the publicity increased, Edith was taken to more and more functions, although by this time she was wheelchair bound. It was said by those that organised these functions that she was enjoying it all, but now, in her mid-nineties, she was becoming extremely tired of it as well. It could be said that the organisers found it more enjoyable than she did, as most observers would agree.

The end of the 80s saw an interesting decade with the Thatcher years, Gorbachev, Glasnost, the world's worst nuclear accident at Chernobyl and the Falklands War. There was an increasing awareness of greenhouse gases and the environment. The year of 1982 saw the 80th anniversary of the sinking of the Titanic with Edith attending more functions in Weymouth and at the Hilton Hotel in Southampton. When she wasn't guest of honour at these functions, she had Titanic enthusiasts visiting her at home. She was now living with her daughter, Dorothy at her home and, at other times, in a nursing home. Some of those that visited her were real enthusiasts, others perhaps more interested in making money.

Edith was by now quite immobile and was taken everywhere by wheelchair, signing never-ending autographs on scraps of paper or whatever came to hand. It was indeed a busy time for her. Perhaps the most moving time for her was in 1993 when she was presented with her father's gold watch at a publicity function at the Hilton Hotel. There were tears in her eyes as she received the watch at the luncheon, remembering her father had always worn it, and the last time she had seen him, he was calmly standing on the boat deck of the Titanic smoking a cigar. The gold watch that had been presented to her would not be hers to keep, however. Being insured for 100 000 pounds, it would be kept in a museum and only brought out for public occasions.

In 1996 Edith's second eldest son, Kenneth, died from Alzheimer's disease aged 75 and would be the fourth of her children whom she had outlived. Edith was now very frail and it was thought by many that the publicity surrounding her should now come to an end. In 1995 Edith received an invitation from the American salvage group, RMS Titanic to go on a short cruise to the Titanic site. Edith left Southampton Airport, accompanied by her youngest daughter, Dorothy on 22 August 1996, bound for New York via Amsterdam. After arrival in New York they spent a few days in a hotel before boarding the 31 000-ton liner, Island Breeze. Edith had finally set sail on her last ocean voyage, heading for a position in the North Atlantic, marked on the chart as, 41 46' N 50 14' W. On reaching this point in the ocean, the Island Breeze stopped, below them lay the wreck of the Titanic in darkness and at peace. On board the Island Breeze were a few dignitaries and the last one or two survivors.

Edith, sitting in her wheelchair, attended a service, which was held on the open deck for those 1500 souls who had perished at this place 84 years ago. The memories came flooding back to her of that nightmare which took place here on 15 April 1912. After the service, she was helped to the ship's rail and, peering down, let a wreath fall from her hands to the dark waters below in memory of her dear father. She was overcome and wept silently, as she again thought of how her father must have fought for his life, along with 1500 other souls, in these icy waters of the North Atlantic. It had always been her lifelong desire to pay her last respects to her dear departed father, and now, 84 years later, her life's dream had been achieved. She had finally carried it out.

On 27 October Edith received a telegram from the Queen congratulating her on

Left: Edith, after letting a wreath fall onto the waters above the Titanic site.

Below: Edith, fifth from right, onboard Island Breeze at Captain's table en route to Titanic site.

her 100th birthday. The celebrations were held at the Hilton Hotel in Southampton and well wishers came from many parts, including America and Australia. One of the guests was Princess Elletra Marconi, the daughter of the radio pioneer, without whose invention, it was doubtful if anyone would have survived that fateful night.

At 7.30 p.m. on 20 January 1997, Edith passed away quietly in her sleep after suffering from pneumonia. She had left behind four sons and two daughters and 40 grandchildren. Edith had been born into a wealthy family and, one could imagine, would have had a good future to look forward to. However, the sinking of the Titanic had mapped out a very different life for her. She was to live a life of giving and she gave all she had, never asking for anything in return. Destiny had decided that she would go on that long journey through life without wealth, but would instead leave a different and certainly better legacy to those she had left behind - her love, her courage and her resilience. She did just that. To her sons and daughters she was not only a wonderful mother but also a marvellous human being. She left them all proud at being a part of her life.

The End

Postscript:

It has just been disclosed that Southampton City Council in England has named a street after Edith Haisman in the city.

Acknowledgments:

Thanks to my wife Lyn, my family and friends, The Courier-Mail, and to everyone that had a part to play in helping me achieve my dream of telling my mother's story. A special thankyou to Mario for his his patience and help in putting this story together.

All photographs are from the Haisman collection, apart from the one reproduced on page 138 which is by kind permission of The Courier-Mail.

put this to my mother who confirmed that someone, sounding like an Irishman and muttering incoherently, was indeed pulled into her boat, half dead as she put it, and wrapped in a blanket by one of the boats crew. Like many story's over the years about the sinking of the Titanic, there will always be the element of doubt as many of those saved were suffering from stress and trauma. In the light of this, I have decided to give the 'Patrick Doyle' story the benefit of the doubt and have included this coincidence as a purposeful diversion away from the main thrust of my mother's authentic account of events as she remembered them.

Perhaps another 'coincidence' worth a mention was on the occasion of my mother at 99 years of age, being accompanied by my sister on a voyage of remembrance to the Titanic wreck site in 1996 on a ship called the 'Island Breeze.' Eighteen months later, the James Cameron movie, Titanic, also showed a 100 year old lady (Rose in the film) with her daughter, visiting the wreck site!

'Edith Haisman Close' is situated in the Freemantle area of Southampton and just a short walking distance away is no. 9 Norman Road, the house where Fred Fleet, Titanic's lookout who first spotted the iceberg, used to live. After falling on hard times he eventually took his own life.

Today, I live just five minutes walk away from Captain Rostron's grave site, the master of the rescue ship Carpathia who showed great courage by turning his ship around and going at full speed through ice fields to answer Titanic's distress call. Without his instant reactions there may well have been a greater loss of life and perhaps I may not be writing this today.

David Haisman

ADDENDUM

My aim has been to write a refreshing and narrative account of my mother's life and to write it in the way she had told us throughout our lifetimes and in a style to which we know she would have approved. It was after all, to be a dedication to a wonderful caring mother from one of her own children, along with the legacy she had left us and one we would always remember her by. I've included her belief in the after life and we, as a family, would laugh along with her on many of these issues but, that's how she told it and that's the way I've recorded it. Having gathered as much information as possible from those who knew my mother as a younger person, including the elders in my family, we had all agreed that the narrative accounts were as accurate as we could remember them by.

There was for instance, the conversation her parents had with a Titanic passenger and his wife and overhearing their anxiety about a fire in the bunkers, still burning after several days into the voyage. Then there was the nervous woman passenger who felt uneasy onboard the Titanic and wanted to leave the ship at Queenstown in Southern Ireland. After the collision with the iceberg, she was never seen again.

As for the 'Patrick Doyle' story, it was virtually impossible to track this character down who led me to this story some 43 years ago so, some pseudonyms have been used for these particular people. However, as some of these stories appear to be so familiar to James Cameron's movie ' Titanic,' I felt they were important enough to include those similarities into my mother's story.

Whilst I was serving onboard Union Castle Line's 'Cape Town Castle' in 1957, I had a very interesting discussion with an Irish seaman from another ship in the port who claimed his grandfather was a steerage passenger on the Titanic and was pulled from the